*Books by* WILLIAM AND PAUL PADDOCK

Hungry Nations
Famine — 1975!

# Famine—1975!

# Famine—1975!

*America's Decision: Who Will Survive?*

## by William and Paul Paddock

Little, Brown and Company · Boston · Toronto

*Published simultaneously in Canada*
*by Little, Brown & Company (Canada) Limited*

PRINTED IN THE UNITED STATES OF AMERICA

# Contents

PART III

POTENTIAL ROLE OF THE UNITED STATES DURING
THE TIME OF FAMINES

# Preface

In a book of this nature the technical background of the co-authors, brothers, is pertinent. The one is an agronomist and plant pathologist, who has headed a tropical research station and also a school of agriculture in Central America and is now a Washington-based consultant in tropical agricultural development. The other is a retired Foreign Service Officer of the State Department, with nearly all of his experience in the developing countries of Asia and Africa, including Russia and Communist China. Combined, we have totaled some forty years of working and traveling in the undeveloped, hungry nations on all continents.

The editorial "we" becomes awkward for two authors when the illustrations out of personal experience obviously demand the forthright "I." So, disregarding the confusion that arises from using the first person singular in events happening on different hemispheres in the same time period, read them as they come. "I" can mean either one of us.

After every two or three years of work in the undeveloped world I return home to my native Iowa.

Each time I am amazed again at the incredible richness of the landscape there. No place in all the world matches the agricultural wealth of the Middle West, a thousand miles and more of deep, rich soil, level terrain and stable climate. In contrast, the areas I know in Asia, Latin America and Africa usually contain only a few square miles of fruitful soil for every hundred square miles of useless land, plus a climate that is a gamble. And sometimes an entire nation has no good land anywhere at all.

I know full well the grinding poverty which is the principal crop from the thin, deficient soils and the undependable rainfall, a poverty which afflicts equally farmers and townfolk. I am also familiar with the spiraling pleas from the despairing people of the undeveloped world for food from us, for technicians, for investment capital, pleas that the resources of our country be sent forth to augment their own paltry assets.

The great material wealth of the United States, derived out of our rich land, has served me and my compatriots well. How best can this wealth serve others?

Today, government officials in Washington are expanding their thinking as to how our abundance can help mankind. I hope this book will aid those who do not yet realize the great constructive power contained in our agricultural richness. Yet, as the hungry nations each day become more hungry, I also want this book to give pause to those who overestimate the extent of our resources, of our capacity to help our fellow men. We do indeed have great power, but the hungry maw outside our borders is beyond the ability of even our abundance to satisfy. Therefore, in the best pioneer tradition, great daring and inventiveness are needed if our aid is to be channeled effectively to the needy ones. This is indeed a challenge worthy of our pride in America.

# Famine—1975!

# Prologue

Power is a tricky, short-time affair. By its very concept it is temporary. When the energy lessens, in whatever fashion it is applied, the power slacks off and things grind to a halt.

Especially in the realm of international politics.

Empires wax and wane. The sources of international power change from one age to the next. And the basis of power is reflected in the names given by historians. The Bronze Age. The Iron Age. The Age of Chivalry. The Age of Discovery. The Age of Steam.

Alexander the Great and Genghis Khan left behind empires that lasted for several centuries, although broken up into units of practical size. Yet similarly great military leaders like Richard the Lion-Heart and Tamerlane are remembered merely as raiders because they left no basis of power behind them. The "empires" of Napoleon and Hitler ended with their downfall. Byzantium lasted a thousand years in the full panoply of relative stability; its rival, the Vatican, seems in comparison a cardboard pageant with its power derived from elusive religiosity and the seesaw art of intrigue. Great Britain came out the victor in the spoils of the Age of Discovery, with Portugal and Holland left in the unimportant corners of the world, with Spain impotent and with France accepting the leavings.

The First World War pitilessly revealed French economic and social obsolescence, British industrial decay, and the gulf between German technological sophistication and political primitiveness. It ended by displaying the dwarfishness of even the strongest of European powers when scaled against America.

History is all an enchanting kaleidoscope — after it is safely in the libraries. At the moment of happening the beast is a different sort of thing.

Today we are in the Atomic Age.

When that first bomb fell on Hiroshima I was attached to the Embassy in Moscow. Like most Americans everywhere I and my fellow officers were awestruck with the news of this bombing; it would shorten the war; it was evidence of our nation's power; we thought only of its value at that particular moment. Quite otherwise was the reaction of our chargé d'affaires, George Kennan. He called together an officers' staff meeting that morning and for an hour he extemporaneously analyzed, actually just thinking aloud, the implications of this new, extraordinary element of force. His strength of intellect, which has since made him prominent in world affairs and academic circles, immediately grasped that the explosion of this single atom bomb had changed irrevocably the sources of international power. As I remember that morning, he forecast the future just about as it has since developed, but to my own discredit I then believed only a part of what he was saying.

The modern world moves fast. How long will we live within the Atomic Age? How long will it be before the possession of atomic weapons (and all the complex economic and scientific apparatus that support those weapons) gives way to a new basis for gauging the relative importance of nations one with another?

This will come about, obviously, whenever a new element or factor appears in world affairs that makes the possession of something else, whatever it may be, of greater strategical value than having a preponderance of atomic weapons.

That new element is already on the horizon. In fact, I forecast a specific date, 1975, when the new crisis will be upon us in all its awesome importance.

Out of this crisis will come the Next Age.

Which, then, will be the dominant world powers, which the dominated?

PART II

# Inevitability of Famine in the Hungry Nations

> . . . and it shall come to pass that, when they shall be hungry, they shall fret themselves, and curse their King and their God . . .
>
> ISAIAH 8:21

# 1

## The Population-Food Collision Is Inevitable: It Is Foredoomed

Not too far in the future from now a strange phenomenon came to a head in parts of the United States. The experts had foreseen the threat of catastrophe that would come about. The press had long quoted experts but usually on the inside pages. Debates had occurred in Congress but not in the strident voices of urgency. People had been worrying but always the worrying was tempered with "something will happen" to forestall the troubles. In this day and age of extraordinary scientific breakthroughs all assumed something was bound to be discovered in time. And so it was especially terrifying when the hospitals of Tacoma and Memphis suddenly filled with the dying and the maimed. Emergency wards were set up in the schools and teams of doctors rushed in from neighboring cities and the federal government mobilized a dozen bureaucracies to cope with the disaster and troops patrolled the streets to control looting. The surrounding countryside was not fully aware of the extent of the trouble until the refugees came flowing out from the cities seeking safety — at first the well-to-do and finally even the poorest people walking on foot and bent under their bundles of whatever they could carry. Yet the countryside did not provide safety because soon here also the danger overwhelmed the population. By the end of the year the trouble was compounded when suddenly Seattle and St. Louis also fell before the scourge and a new focus of disaster appeared first in Buffalo and then Albany. Now the government cordoned off the refugees because even their appearance in an untroubled area would set off a panic. Few in the still safe regions would extend help to the fleeing. The economy of the nation slowed and weakened as every man centered his attention on his own safety, on the safety of his own family.

The foregoing is a rather loose description of what happened in the old days whenever yellow fever plagues broke out in, for instance, New Orleans. Maybe this is what will be happening some day in the future when air pollution makes certain cities unlivable and the scientific breakthroughs to control it do not, after all, come about and the various levels of government are not, after all, able to stop the causes of pollution.

For 1975, however, this would be a close description of what will be happening in parts of the undeveloped world because of famine and its accompanying civil unrest. Change the name of the cities from Tacoma and Albany to Madras and Recife.

Worse, the catastrophe of these forthcoming famines and unrest will have one characteristic different from previous plagues and disasters. Until now such troubles were overcome and finished within, usually, a year or two. Famines, for instance, would cease with the next year's harvest or, at most, at the end of the rather short cycle of bad drought years.

The famines which are now approaching will not, in contrast, be caused by weather variations and therefore will not be ended in a year or so by the return of normal rainfall. They will last for years, perhaps several decades, and they are, for a surety, inevitable. Ten years from now parts of the undeveloped world will be suffering from famine. In fifteen years the famines will be catastrophic and revolutions and social turmoil and economic upheavals will sweep areas of Asia, Africa, and Latin America.

This is not a book on the population explosion. Neither is it a book on development of the undeveloped countries, nor is it a book on food production. It deals, instead, with the *consequences* of the world's inability to cope with these problems before the famines strike. It deals with the policies that must be formulated in Washington (as the true center of today's leadership and power) in order to alleviate the famines and to shorten their length.

A locomotive is roaring full throttle down the track. Just around the bend an impenetrable mudslide has oozed across the track.

There it lies, inert, static, deadly. Nothing can stop the locomotive in time. Collision is inevitable. Catastrophe is foredoomed. Miles back up the track the locomotive could have been warned and stopped. Years ago the mud-soaked hill could have been shored up to forestall the landslide. Now it is too late.

The locomotive roaring straight at us is the population explosion. The unmovable landslide across the tracks is the stagnant production of food in the undeveloped nations, the nations where the population increases are greatest.

The collision is inevitable. The famines are inevitable.

It is a difficult task to convince the government official, the learned scientist, the journalist or the bewildered man in the street that a collision between exploding population and static agriculture is imminent. Always they refer to some aspect of our complex world economy or of our scientific span of knowledge that is going to deflect the famines from happening with full force. Always, it seems, the scientist who is indeed an expert in his own branch of knowledge nevertheless naïvely takes for granted that the solution lies ready for use in another branch of science.

This was, as a pertinent example, the case with me personally. In December 1965 I welcomed the invitation to attend a conference at Cornell University on the agricultural potentials of the tropics. The conference was broadly based in the sense that experts from many scientific disciplines took part. As an agronomist I know the limitations of increasing food production rapidly, especially the long time-lag between discovery of an improved technique and its final utilization out in the fields; also I have long been acquainted with the troubles of the tropical world and realize that these troubles are due primarily to limitations imposed by soil and climate or, to say it another way, our lack of know-how in coping with tropical conditions.

In my opening paper at this conference I stressed that the potentials of tropical agriculture, based on today's knowledge, are limited, but I expressed the hope that the experts from other sciences would have helpful ideas that could bring progress to the tropics quickly.

That evening I had dinner with one of the country's leading

demographers, J. Mayone Stycos. "This is going to be a most significant conference," he said, "because we are going to need a solution to the food problem *fast*."

"Don't expect any food solution to come out of this conference," I said, "for the direct reason that there is none in sight. Whatever new ideas are presented here will not change the agricultural outlook in the next ten or twenty years. What I want to learn here is the methods which the demographers like you have on tap. How can you curtail population growth so that we agriculturalists will have time to solve the food problem?"

"*Us!*" Stycos nearly shouted across the table. "We have *nothing* that will work in the next ten years. We have been counting on the agronomists to give the population men enough time."

Stycos then leafed through some clippings he took from his pocket. "Look here. The Secretary of Agriculture, Freeman, has just made a speech at the FAO Conference in Rome. He said: 'Some newly developing countries are already increasing their agricultural production at rates higher than those ever achieved by the highly developed nations — including my own.' " [1]

I replied, "No matter what is said in public and for whatever reason, the true situation is that food production in the undeveloped world is nearly static. I *know* the food possibilities in these countries. I *know* that future food increases, based on today's techniques, are limited and can only change slowly."

Hereupon I took out of my briefcase my own handful of clippings. "What about all these statements from the demographers? This one claims that in most of the world man's fertility will decline in the next five or ten years[2] and this one says we have one or two generations ahead of us before the number of people become hopeless." [3]

Stycos's answer was simply, "It isn't so. This I *know*. Fertility may decline a little, but mortality will decline even more. The net result in the next ten years will be an increase in the number of people greater than anything the world has ever dreamed of."

I asked, "What if the governments, especially the U.S., gave all the money needed, eliminated all the bureaucratic bottlenecks, did away with all the religious taboos, everyone gave fullest support?

Could this stop the overpopulation in time to avoid the famines?"

Stycos leaned back, thought for a while and said slowly, "As a demographer I would relish such support. Yes, by 1975 you might lower the birth rate by a few points. In a region like Central America you might reduce the birth rate from fifty to forty-five or even forty per thousand in ten years. That would be a major, a truly major achievement."

I said this was not enough.

Stycos added, "Of course, it would accumulate and go down faster after that."

My own answer was that this still would not be fast enough. The world's margin of food supplies will already have been passed in ten years.

Regarding valid experts basing their hopes in provinces other than their own, it is pertinent that Roger Revelle, director of the Harvard Center for Population Studies, when he testified on this subject before the Committee on Agriculture of the House of Representatives, spoke primarily of hopes not in his own field, that is, population control, but in his hopes for increasing food production, a field in which he is not trained.[4]

Today twelve thousand people died of hunger in the world. Tomorrow another twelve thousand will die.[5]

These deaths, however, are nothing more than the warning whistle of the locomotive rushing down the tracks toward the immovable landslide of static food production in the hungry nations. There is neither a new agricultural method nor is there a birth control technique on the horizon which can avert the inevitable famines.

Don't call this pessimism. It is merely sad realism.

"We are in the presence, perhaps, of a turning-point in human affairs so immense that we do not perceive it: 1966 may be the year in which sufficiency in food disappears from the world and famine becomes a recurrent and habitual condition. No doubt those not immediately affected will 'learn to live with it,' as with the housing shortage or overcrowded schools. No doubt — for a decade at least — actual starvation will be rare and localized, and disaster on the grand scale will be forestalled by modern means of transport and by emergency actions. . . . But, once the overall trend is the wrong way, it will get progressively harder to reverse." [6]

So much has been written about the population explosion. The columns of statistics, the plethora of data. By now, even the most serious worriers are dulled with the flow of percentages and the trends and the graphs.

The natural reaction is to turn wearily away to other matters. Yet, as with a tumor, the stinging effect of the population explosion will not die down. It continues to eat the vitals. Always the hour of crisis moves closer. Each new set of statistics, of facts, merely illustrates that previous estimates of the increases in population have been too low.

In 1947 I was stationed in Kabul. We at the American Embassy were caught in an argument between our friends the British and our friends the Afghans. This particular incident concerned the size of the population of Afghanistan. No census had ever been taken. Whose guesswork were we to believe?

A drought had developed and the Afghan government had appealed to the Embassy for flour. Washington immediately agreed, and the British also immediately promised to facilitate shipment through the port of Karachi and to forward the flour by rail to Quetta and Peshawar, the only practical routes into landlocked, remote Afghanistan.

Everyone was in accord as to the percentage of Afghan population that was affected by this drought and in need of relief. But how many people were there? The Afghans claimed the country's population totaled 10 million. The British said, "Nonsense." Their long-accepted estimate was 7 million. The Afghan officials said their figure was based on the number of people vaccinated in a cholera scare the previous year, when even the nomads were vaccinated. The British still claimed 7 million.

The difference of over 25 per cent was important, not only for the amount of flour to be shipped from the United States but, equally important, for the amount of dock and railroad space the British were to arrange for transshipment. This was the year of the division of the Raj into independent Pakistan and independent

India. Communal riots were erupting all over the subcontinent and the harried British were noble even to give time and effort to facilitate these shipments into Afghanistan.

Anyway, the flour, especially packaged in sealed cans to survive the hot Red Sea passage, did arrive from Karachi, through the Khyber Pass, across the Jalalabad Desert, over the Lattaband Pass and down to Kabul. It was distributed to the bakeries around the country. The crisis ebbed and passed — not, for the record, due to the American flour which turned out to be of a type the Afghans did not know how to use for bread, although eventually it was all consumed.

But the distribution through the bakers definitely proved that Afghanistan's population was much more than 7 million and, in fact, over 10 million (today it is over 15 million).

When you read any population figure from an undeveloped country, add to it! And also from anywhere else. For instance: "Recent population projections [for the U.S.] for the end of the century have ranged all the way from 263 million to 388 million, but most experts are reluctant to be pinned down to long-term figures, pointing out that the most reliable study in the early '40's projected a population of 165 million for the year 2000 — a figure exceeded more than a decade ago." [7] As recently as 1964, United States officials were talking about a world population of 6 billion people in the year 2000. Today they say it will be 7 billion!

The easiest statistic to grasp is the one that tells in how many years the population of a country will double. It illustrates, for one thing, how quickly the country must double the amount of food it produces in order to maintain the current level of nutrition, however low that may be (in addition, of course, to doubling the number of houses, schools, sanitation facilities, etc.).

What if the population of the Netherlands were to double in twenty years? Aside from where to put the new people in that already pressed-together country, could its currently thriving economy and its equitable social structure possibly absorb all the strains such a population influx would cause? One result would surely be a drastic lowering of Holland's present living standard. Yet in the field of urban organization Holland has, I guess, about the most efficient, most intelligent government to be found anywhere, and its regulations to govern city and rural planning have long been refined to a degree undreamed of in the United States or elsewhere.

If the experienced Hollanders could barely cope with a population doubling within a generation, the outlook is indeed gloomy for the weak governments and uneducated communities of Honduras, Ceylon, the Ivory Coast, and also the miscellaneous corners like the Fiji Islands, Martinique, and — you name it!

A momentous date with the world's birth control experts was 1957, the year the first widespread testing of the new intrauterine coil for women was completed (this is a small, inexpensive plastic loop or coil, simple and quick for a doctor to insert, requiring little attention once in place, and is 85 per cent effective in preventing conception).

Taking 1957 as our benchmark, the accompanying table gives the year when the populations of the following most prolific countries will have *doubled*.[8]

The first adequate population forecasts were based on an effort

### PREDICTED POPULATION DOUBLING DATES

| | |
|---|---|
| Costa Rica | 1973 |
| Burundi | 1974 |
| Syria | 1974 |
| Mauritania | 1975 |
| Libya | 1976 |
| Taiwan | 1977 |
| Dominican Republic | 1977 |
| Ivory Coast | 1977 |
| Mali | 1977 |
| Venezuela | 1978 |
| Vietnam | 1978 |
| Honduras | 1979 |
| Malaysia | 1979 |
| Mexico | 1979 |
| Mongolia | 1979 |
| Panama | 1979 |
| Philippines | 1979 |
| Brazil | 1980 |

at a worldwide census in 1950. When in 1960 the second world-wide census was taken, most of the earlier predictions had to be discarded because the new data showed a faster growth rate than had previously been thought possible.

Venezuela had believed on the basis of the 1950 census that its population would double in 26 years; now the 1960 census showed a doubling in 18. Korea 25 years instead of 50. India 33 years instead of 54. Peru 27 years instead of 37.[9]

India during this decade between the two censuses had increased its population 20.5 per cent — in contrast to 13.3 per cent in the preceding decade.[10]

Nigeria's 1963 census pulled a startling surprise for that country's planners. The census counted 56 million people — 19 million more than the highest estimate had anticipated.[11]

In 1958 the United Nations estimated that in 1970 the population of "the less developed world" would be 2,950,000,000; in 1965 this figure was revised upward to 3,070,000,000.[12]

An important lesson must be hammered home from these figures. Inaccurate as population statistics in the hungry nations may be, the evidence shows them to be on the low, on the conservative, side. Looking at them realistically, they indicate only one trend: the locomotive of population explosion is gaining momentum faster each day.

There are several dynamics making this inevitable.

## Population Dynamic Number One: The Death Rate

Recently, I visited in Washington the library of the Population Reference Bureau and asked for some information on death rates in the developing countries. This Bureau is the mother lode of all population information and it has been the spearhead, thanks to its president, Robert Cook, in awakening the American public to the dangers of uncontrolled human fertility.

"You want to know about death rates! Great!" they said. "We've been trying for years to get people interested in death rates, to get people to understand that the 'explosion' is due primarily to falling death rates and not to changing birth rates."

With everyone's preoccupation over birth control, we all seem to

ignore the fact that the death rate is still dynamic, *still* going down.
The end result is the same as an increase in birth rates.

Until this century the history of the world had been pockmarked
by a steady series of afflictions from plague, cholera, diphtheria,
smallpox and other pestilences. However, it now has been half a
century since the world has had a major pandemic with a significant toll of deaths (when 25 million died of influenza in 1919).[13]
Few people can grasp the dramatic speed with which death rates
have fallen, especially in the undeveloped countries. It all came
about overnight.

By 1948 it was clear that a new interest in health work existed in
many countries where no such interest had existed before the war . . .
Mass inoculations required little coercion. The efficiency of DDT and
antibiotics in control of infections was known because of our war experience. And the significance of BCG for tuberculosis was also
known. But no one realized their full potentialities in 1948.

It was clear, by 1948, that the death rates in the non-industrial countries could be made to decline — but no one knew how rapidly. No one
knew how well the controls effected by such agents as DDT would be
accepted. No one fully realized that mass public health controls could
produce such rapid and widespread results. Japan, which is not a "non-
industrial" country, had a crude death rate of 8.9 in 1952 — half of
that which existed in 1946. Ceylon, perhaps a better example, had a
death rate of only 10.14 in 1954 — half of its 1946 rate. These changes
were hardly predictable in 1948.[14]

The effectiveness of modern-day medicine — the rapidity with
which it can be disseminated and the eagerness with which people
accept it — has resulted in the drastic changes in the death rates
shown in the table.

FALLING DEATH RATES IN THE HUNGRY WORLD[15]
(per thousand)

|  | 1935 | 1950 | 1965 | 1980* |
|---|---|---|---|---|
| World | 25 | 19 | 16 | 12.7 |
| Asia | 33 | 23 | 20 | 13 |
| Africa | 33 | 27 | 23 | 18 |
| Latin America | 22 | 19 | 12 | 8.2 |

* Projected.

# SCHEMATIC PRESENTATION OF BIRTH AND DEATH RATES IN LESS DEVELOPED COUNTRIES

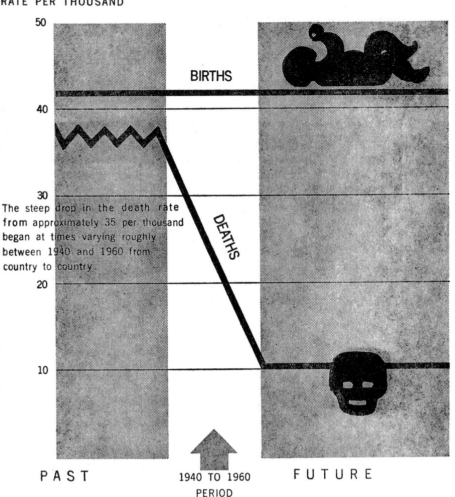

RATE PER THOUSAND

50

40

BIRTHS

30

The steep drop in the death rate from approximately 35 per thousand began at times varying roughly between 1940 and 1960 from country to country

DEATHS

20

10

PAST

1940 TO 1960
PERIOD

FUTURE

The contrast between the plummeting death rates and the near static birth rates is illustrated in the graph on page 17.

The drop in death rates has been so spectacular that many believe they cannot go lower. On the contrary, despite the straight lines in the graph (from a publication of the National Academy of Sciences)[16] trends show not only room for a further fall of the death rate but a clear forecast that it *will* fall.

Look at the low death rates already achieved in the following four undeveloped countries:[17]

| | |
|---|---|
| Taiwan | 5.7 per thousand |
| Ceylon | 8.7 |
| Hong Kong | 4.9 |
| Singapore | 5.7 |

These low death rates are due in part to the populations having today a higher percentage of young people (as discussed later in this chapter). But another major factor is better medical care; and what these countries have achieved, the other undeveloped areas will strive also to achieve. The table of current death rates below shows how much room for a further dynamic fall is possible.

### 1965 DEATH RATES[18]
(per thousand)

| | |
|---|---|
| El Salvador | 10.8 |
| Guatemala | 17.3 |
| Mexico | 10.4 |
| Chile | 12.0 |
| Ivory Coast | 35.0 |
| Senegal | 23-29 |
| Upper Volta | 27-31 |
| Iran | 23-27 |
| India | 21-23 |
| Indonesia | 19-23 |
| South Korea | 11-13 |

If by 1975 the "death rate in Guatemala fell somewhere near the 1950 United States level [9.6][19] — a not unlikely development —

this alone would increase the number of women reaching the beginning of the child-bearing period by 36 per cent and the number at the end of the child-bearing period by 85 per cent. . . . This drop in the death rate in the child-bearing period has and will have in the next few years a gigantic effect on the birth rate." [20]

The mortality rates remain dynamic. They will continue their downward rush in the years ahead — until checked by famine.

A friend of mine, a charming lady in her fifties who had never traveled in the undeveloped world, happened to do an important favor for a member of the family of a ruling potentate of one of the semi-backward nations (whom I would like to name but it probably would not be of benefit to him). She was invited to visit the royal family and gladly accepted. Her plane arrived at evening and the ride to the palace through the capital city, pleasantly exotic in the half-light, was a delight despite the clouds of dust swirling everywhere. At dinner with the highly cultured ruler and his wife and children she was told the rainy season was long overdue, and the next morning the first rains did burst forth. Afterwards, she took a walk outside the palace gate and along the rutted main street and saw people eagerly scooping up the water out of the puddles along with the horse manure and anything else that had happened to accumulate during the dry season. They used the water for cooking, for drinking, for, in a word, normal living. Sickened, my friend asked the ruler why he allowed this, why he did not provide sanitation facilities and clean water at least in his capital city. After all, this was not a destitute country; compared to many it was recognized as prosperous. The ruler replied, "I know it is not pleasant to see people drinking from the ruts in the road, and we do have enough money at least to change things here in the city. But the problem is not that simple. Rather, I have not been sure in my own mind how to handle this problem. So I have visited other countries, especially India, to see what happens when a city gets pure drinking water. My decision was that when India learns how to feed all of the people who have been kept alive because of the good water, then I shall order a modern water system here." My friend was not convinced this was right but she was intelligent enough to accept it as a thought-out policy.

My own opinion is that this ruler is an **exceedingly** wise man.

Although he could never announce such a policy publicly, he has, in various ways, held back spending tax moneys on public health. Some hospitals and clinics have been built and staffed by aid-giving countries and the aura of progress in medical services is believed in by the local people. Yet there has been no all-out effort by the government along these lines; this must be a major factor why the population increase rate is not out of hand and why the nation, compared to its neighbors, is relatively prosperous.

## Population Dynamic Number Two: The Younger Generation

The people are already here who will cause the famines. Birth control techniques are for the future; they cannot affect the present millions of hungry stomachs.

Today, nearly half of the people in the undeveloped world are under the age of fifteen years. Dr. B. R. Sen, director-general of the Food and Agriculture Organization of the United Nations (FAO), says: "Even if birth control measures were adopted on a wide scale, population would still increase substantially because of the large number of children who will be forming their own families ten, twenty and thirty years from now." [21]

In Latin America, for instance, the increasing percentage of children in the population means that by 1975 there will be 60 per cent *more* marriages formed than in 1960.[22] The potential for further population increase is truly enormous.

By 1975 Latin America (and most of the undeveloped world as well) will find itself in the position of a friend of mine who is now a professor at one of the leading universities. John returned from World War II in 1946, was married and settled down to a serious graduate study program. In the subsidized days of the G.I. Bill and the confidence of a returning marine, he had four children in quick succession. After a stint in the business world he accepted an excellent teaching position. His salary moved up to $10,000 in 1955 and to $15,000 by 1960. He made a down payment on his house and was marked as a comer in his profession. By 1965 he was making $20,000 — a fine record for someone only fifteen years out of graduate school, a good record for anyone!

In 1965 his first child entered college. It cost John $2,500 a year. In 1966 his second child entered college. Now it was costing him $5,000 a year for education, a real financial burden for this hard-working, energetic professor. By 1967 when his third child is in college it will cost him $7,500 a year. Now his savings will be gone and he will take out another mortgage on his house. And when his last child enters college, his 1968 education bill will come to $10,000 a year! A $20,000 salary does not go far under such circumstances.

The hungry world is in a position similar to John's. The only difference, really, is that when John has his fourth child educated, he can begin to recoup his savings. The hungry world's problem is just beginning and the time of recoupment will not be in this century.

By farming farther and farther up the hillsides (until all the extra land is used up), by borrowing more and more funds from the international agencies (until credit is exhausted), by receiving from the well-fed countries more and more of their surplus food (but now the surplus is about gone), the hungry world has been able to keep its children alive. But the children are getting bigger, they eat more, they need more calories to stay alive and now there are more and more of them and, worse, even the children themselves are having children. The family grows ever larger and so do the problems of the parent country.

Therefore, between now and 1975 we shall see much of the hungry world exhaust its capacity to cope with the population that is *already* here, that is already eating, that is demanding more at the dawn of each day. This is the built-in inevitability of the dynamic of today's generation.

## Population Dynamic Number Three: The Birth Rate

Until the 1950's the maximum birth rate physiologically possible in a population was believed to be forty-five births per thousand.

For the classical European population it was quite simple to calculate: out of every thousand people there were 500 women; of these 410 were either too young or too old for child-bearing or were, for some reason, non-fertile; another 45 had just had a child and there was not time to conceive and deliver another in the current year.

In 1945, then, the 45 per thousand figure was fixed in academic circles as the formula for the maximum possible birth rate.

By the 1950's, though, this was refuted in the undeveloped nations. Today, a dozen countries have birth rates above the 45 figure. The numbers 48, 49, 50 appear in the statistics. No one really knows how the women manage these figures. But they do. Costa Rica's birth rate, for example, in 1940 was 44.9; in 1950 it was 49.2; in 1960 it was 50.0; today it is 50.2.[23]

Part of the blame can be placed on the higher percentage of young people found in these populations today (thus, a larger reproductive age group). Another part of the blame probably comes from our having each year a more accurate set of birth statistics. But yet another part can be placed on improved health. Healthy people are simply more fertile. Good health decreases the number of stillbirths, miscarriages, and spontaneous abortions. Good health increases the frequency of intercourse.[24]

Although improved living conditions, such as those sometimes brought on by industrialization, are often given as a reason for a decreased birthrate, actually the evidence seems to be the opposite. As industrialization breaks down traditional social patterns, there is first of all, apparently, an increase in the birth rate. A couple of decades later the birth rate may fall off, but not at first. For example, changes in the social pattern can bring about greater marital stability to non-legal unions; or, as in India, the breakdown of taboos on the remarriage of widows could raise the number of births in the population.[25]

Although the reasons behind the dynamism of the increases in birth rate are still vague and uncertain, the statistics of their reality are clear.

## Population Dynamic Number Four: Man's Reproductive System

Man has been evolving and reproducing for a million years. Those who expect science to be able to find quickly a birth control method which can successfully circumvent this million years of such single-mindedness both overestimate modern science and underestimate the efficiency of the reproductive system which evolution has provided man.

\*    \*    \*

Most of us have been confident that science soon will find some effective way to control births because we cannot bring ourselves to believe the appalling population figures projected for the coming generation. We have fallen back on the hope that "something" will be devised quickly to limit the statistics.

Let me now do away with such false hopes for the coming decade.

## The False Hope of Limited Families

Most important, we forget that people love children. This is a key characteristic that man and his wife have acquired through the million years of evolution. The simple love for children itself guarantees this book's predictions.

Surveys in undeveloped countries indicate that nearly always the average woman does not become concerned with family planning until she has four or five children. In Chile, for instance, interviews have shown that the people there consider the ideal number of children per family is four. Forty-two per cent of the families in that country have not achieved this ideal.[26] In rural India the preferred number averages above four.[27]

Thus, we can assume that with the "perfect" birth control method available to all, 42 per cent of the Chilean parents would still not want to use it — and similar data shows that neither would the average Indian farm wife unless she already had four children. Their reasons for this ideal figure for a family have nothing to do with the cost of bringing up the children, with the teachings of the Catholic Church (in Chile), privacy of parents in the homes, etc. People *love* children.

Also, it is discouraging to note that certain societies demand surplus children.

In many countries, grown-up children who will support their aged parents are the chief form of social security. If a man and his wife do

not have at least one adult male child, they have little to look forward
to when they can no longer work to support themselves. Under conditions of high child mortality, the average married couple needs to produce many children to be sufficiently certain that at least one adult boy
will survive to become a man. Only in this way can they ensure their
own future security. Whenever infant and child mortality can be
brought down to a low enough level, the probability in an individual
family that a male child will survive becomes very much greater, and
the pressure for large numbers of children correspondingly lessens. This
is one of the principal reasons the profession of public health needs to
be deeply involved in the problems of family planning and population
control.[28]

## The False Hope of the IUD

The intrauterine device (IUD) for women is the big hope today
among population experts working in the undeveloped countries.
It is already widely accepted, factories are under construction in
many countries to mass-produce it cheaply. This is the only thing
on the horizon which looks as if it might make a fast enough impact on birth rates in the foreseeable future in the hungry nations.
But . . .

They cannot insert the IUD's fast enough!

Dr. Alan F. Guttmacher, president of Planned Parenthood–
World Population, recently told a Senate committee how impressed he was with the speed with which the IUD can be inserted.
He told of seeing a Chinese woman doctor with a team of well-
trained nurses make insertions in seventy-five patients in three
hours.[29] That averages out as one patient every two minutes and
twenty-four seconds. Dr. Jack Lippes, the inventor of the most
widely used type of IUD, states that a physician can insert one
IUD every six minutes.[30]

Neither of these two figures is fast enough.

Each year in India an additional 850,000 women enter childbear-
ing age.[31] Dr. Lippes says: "The greatest shortage in India is time.
The birth control revolution must be instituted in less than ten
years. If in ten years India adds another 200 million people to its
population, neither India nor her friends will be able to feed these
new numbers." [32] He adds that a program of 25 million coil inser-

tions by 1969 could lead to a real drop in the Indian birth rate.

Such a target figure would be a true achievement, but current trends and the current slow tempo of India's governmental organizations would seem to make it unrealistic. Progress of this program, however, can be checked upon before 1969. Dr. Lippes expects 3 million insertions to be made in 1966 and 6 million in 1967.[33] It will be indicative of India's ability to handle such a program if these figures are achieved, figures which are huge elsewhere but modest in view of India's crisis.

In addition to the unproven ability of the Indian government to operate such a crash program, there is also the problem of the lack of medical personnel available for this work. Since it is believed that the insertion of the IUD is sufficiently delicate to require a physician, a key to the success of any such program depends on the number of doctors available, and this I discuss later.

An extra complication in India which has not received much publicity is that women are reluctant to let male doctors insert the coils. Yet India has only about eight thousand women doctors.[34] As in most other countries, a large proportion of these doctors do not want to move from the cities to the villages, the place where the most serious part of the problem lies.[35]

India is perhaps an unfair example. Everything seems so much harder in India!

At the other extreme is Taiwan, also an untypical example.

[Taiwan] has an ideal setting for a family planning program: fundamental to the success of any attempt to slow population growth are the social and economic conditions and attitudes which determine individual family size. Taiwan is going through a transition from a traditional to a modern society. The island is becoming industrialized to a great extent. Literacy and education are widespread, and the transportation and communication systems are good.[36]

Taiwan is considered such an ideal example that as many as a hundred foreign visitors a month sometimes come to study its family planning program.[37] Yet Taiwan expects to insert less than 150,-000 IUD's in 1967. Thus, what will be the end result of this "ideal" situation? ". . . even with an intensive family planning program to accelerate the present decline in the birth rate, the population [of Taiwan] will still double before the turn of the century." [38]

And do not forget the coil is not recommended for use until after a woman has already given birth to a child, thus lessening the percentage able to take advantage of it. And of those who do, 30 per cent lose or remove the IUD within the first year.[39]

Unfortunately, many governments and many aid officials put sole faith in the IUD; they fail to devise overall programs making use of all methods open for population control. In fact, those few governments of the undeveloped areas which have launched tentative birth control programs "seem to have fallen into the 'technological fallacy' which has long marked Western thinking in this area. They have adopted, in other words, a kind of blind faith in gadgetry of contraception." [40]

I offer as an aside the suggestion that retired doctors and nurses from the United States and elsewhere might well be engaged as technicians (by the Peace Corps perhaps) to insert IUD's as part of the population control programs in these countries. Knowledge of the local language would not be necessary. Such a group of medical persons ("The Coil Corps") working full time solely with IUD's could indeed have an impact on a nation or on a single province. The usefulness of the IUD as a birth control program is in direct proportion to the doctors available.

## The False Hope of the Pill

The Pill, it is accepted in most scientific circles, will stop the reproductive process of the Cuzco Indian, the farm maid of Upper Volta and the Balinesian novitiate as effectively as of the Baltimore housewife. However, if any one of these cannot afford to buy a new supply at the end of the week or is illiterate and does not read the directions correctly or just fails, for whatever reason, to take the pills regularly, then all bets are off.

No birth control method needs a stronger motivation than does the present type of the Pill inasmuch as it requires daily attention, hours away from knowing whether or not it is going to be needed. Such motivation is just as scarce in the hungry world as in Baltimore. Thus, it is not entirely a matter of affluence or literacy. Remember also that when a woman goes off the Pill, or forgets to take it regularly, her fertility is heightened!

Yet let us assume that somehow or other the government of an undeveloped country is able to persuade most women to take the Pill. Imagine what would happen if a rumor suddenly spread through the countryside that, after a year's use, the Pill caused cancer or two-headed births. Such a rumor would be difficult if not impossible to correct in an illiterate population. That such a rumor would get started must be accepted as a probability. Consider, for instance, the similar rumors in our country that have circulated, especially when the product of one drug firm (not of the other firms) was questioned by the Department of Health, Education and Welfare.

Actually, the medical profession itself is not united in its opinion about the Pill. The *Medical Letter*, a non-profit drug-advisory service for physicians, said in its February 1966 issue that women for whom the Pill had been prescribed "should be informed of the present status of knowledge about the possible risks involved." In the light of recent reports about clotting, eye damage and related disorders in some users, the publication said, "it is necessary to repeat the advice . . . that women who can satisfactorily use topical contraceptive measures should not use oral [the Pill] contraceptives." [41]

A few years from now there is little doubt the current intensive research in this field will develop new types of pills or injections that will be startlingly effective, such as the current reports of studies on a "morning after" pill, a "monthly" pill, injections valid for a year for both men and women, etc. Unfortunately, today's Pill, successful though it is with individuals, is an unfirm foundation on which to build a nation-wide campaign. Instead, it should be only one part of a program that utilizes actively all varieties of population control.

## The False Hope of Sterilization

In India, "of all the methods tried so far [to control population growth], only sterilization has yielded significant results." [42] In 1957 Madras State started a policy of voluntary subsidized male

sterilizations (a free operation plus a bonus of $7.50, and a three-
to six-day holiday with pay for government employees). Gradually,
other states started similar programs. Also the government in
Delhi, after prolonged procrastination, has now come out in favor
of this and has established a goal of 5,000,000 male sterilizations
by the end of 1970.[43] "Had India embarked on this policy 15
years ago with fervor, the country by now could have cut its birth
rate in half." [44]

The strength of a sterilization program is that it has a cumulative
effect as the men overcome their initial psychological rejection of it
and learn not to be fearful of the operation. It takes, unfortunately,
a determined government, full medical services and a prolonged
education and propaganda campaign in order to achieve significant
results. In this, India is typical. Even with the glaring catastrophe
of overpopulation constantly before them, the officials at Delhi
have only now turned their attention to this campaign which some
of the provincial states had initiated several years earlier.

Now it is too late. India does not have enough doctors for a
massive sterilization program. Nor are the Indian men yet ready to
accept it.

Only Taiwan, Korea and Pakistan of all the other undeveloped
nations have instituted sterilization programs.[45] This can be an important tool in the future, but not in time to stop the famines.


## The False Hope of Japan

At every turn today in the demographic field the phenomenal
success story of the Japanese in achieving a dramatic lowering of
the birth rate is emphasized. Between 1951 and 1961 that country
cut its birth rate in half and will, in fact, by the end of this generation not quite maintain its present population. Those who refuse
to believe the end results of the world's population explosion always say, "If Japan can do it, so can other countries when the need
arises." In fact, even Ronald Freedman, president of the Population Association of America, recently predicted that India and Pakistan are able to go through a fertility decline similar to that in
Japan.[46]

There is not a chance of this, unfortunately, within the time period we are speaking of here.

What did Japan have in its favor which today's hungry nations do not have?

### Japan Is a Tight Little Island.

The Japanese are packed, compressed, into an area the size of Montana with 685 persons per square mile (4 for Montana). Herein lies a basic observation that it does not seem possible for a government to push successfully for a birth control program until the people themselves demand it. This they do not do until everyone is practically standing on top of one another.

The year 1947 was the Moment of Truth for Japan. Upon losing World War II it lost its dreams of expansion. Suddenly, the people realized that their future had to be found *within* their own boundaries. With a birth rate of over 34 per thousand this realization brought a universal groundswell to do "something." It was not simply a movement of sociologists and intellectuals.

No similar feeling of "standing room only" exists in any hungry, undeveloped nation today of which I know. This is usually because most of these nations have a lot of empty (useless) land that gives the illusion that there is plenty of space available for the oncoming populations. This is borne out by one often used, misleading type of statistic, that of population per square mile in a country. Thus, Brazil has only 24 people per square mile, Indonesia 180, Ethiopia 44. Even India (377) has a population density of about half that of Japan.

In the densely populated highlands of Guatemala where I once lived for several years, there is the firm belief that when things get too crowded people can always move to the empty department of the Petén, an area which actually few Guatemalans have ever seen. Only the trained agronomist realizes that, until new agricultural techniques are found, this type of jungle area cannot support more than the few thousand persons now there — which is why, of course, it is empty.

This dangerous illusion of "vast" empty spaces in these countries was typically expressed by the influential N. Viera Altamirano, editor of *El Diario de Hoy* in the capital of continental Latin America's most populated country, El Salvador (330 people per square mile).[47] He wrote that Latin America as a whole needs "two billion more inhabitants" and that the resources of Central America are sufficient for a population ten times her present size.[48] To this I give no comment!

### The Japanese Were Not Adverse to Abortions.

The Japanese people in 1947 did not wait for science to come up with a new gadget, such as the later-developed IUD, to limit man's reproductive capacity. The government legalized abortion in 1948. The results were startling:[49]

| | |
|---|---|
| 1950 | 320,000 abortions |
| 1955 | 1,200,000 abortions |

More than any other single factor, the opportunity to have an abortion performed under safe and easily available conditions and, above all, legally, is the cause of Japan's success in population control. Such a method is completely taboo in much of the hungry world.

### The Japanese Population Is Literate.

Most of the hungry world is illiterate — and it is going to stay illiterate throughout this generation, and probably much longer.

Japan has had a compulsory education program since 1872. Illiteracy is so rare that the census no longer bothers to tabulate it. The last year for which figures were given was 1948 when the illiteracy rate was 1.1 per cent. In contrast Africa's is 84 per cent, Latin America's 40 per cent.[50]

Most demographers affirm that literacy is an important prerequisite for an effective birth control program (although I wonder, as a non-demographer, if this condition cannot be bypassed by other forms of government propaganda).

### Japan Has a Relatively Low Proportion of Farmers.

Farmers everywhere always have more children than city folk. Children are an asset in the rural area where their labor can be used; but they are a liability in the city where they contribute little but consume a major part of the family income. As long ago as

1930 only one out of every three Japanese farmed.[51] Today, in contrast, two out of every three farm in Asia, Africa and Latin America.

*Japan Has a Large Medical Profession.*

Physicians say that trained doctors, not just technicians or nurses, are necessary to the effective application of birth control techniques to a population. If such reasoning is sound (and I am not sure that a corps of technicians could not be trained adequately enough for specific jobs such as insertion of the IUD's), then the undeveloped countries can never expect to catch up in the next ten years with the large number of doctors in Japan. Note the great gap between Japan and these other nations in inhabitants per physician:[52]

PHYSICIANS IN JAPAN AND THE HUNGRY WORLD

|  | Inhabitants Per Physician |
|---|---|
| JAPAN | 900 |
| Mexico | 1,800 |
| Costa Rica | 2,200 |
| Brazil | 2,500 |
| Panama | 2,500 |
| Syria | 5,200 |
| Libya | 5,800 |
| India | 5,800 |
| Malaysia | 6,500 |
| Pakistan | 11,000 |
| Gambia | 16,000 |
| Mauritania | 26,000 |
| Nigeria | 27,000 |
| Vietnam | 29,000 |
| Afghanistan | 32,000 |
| Mali | 39,000 |
| Indonesia | 41,000 |
| Burundi | 66,000 |
| Upper Volta | 76,000 |
| Ethiopia | 96,000 |

*The Japanese Lowered the Size of Their "Ideal" Family.*

At a dinner recently I had the good fortune to be seated next to a most delightful young Japanese wife who, however, seemed to lapse regularly into moments of preoccupation. The dinner was for her husband, who had just completed his graduate work, and the two were returning the following week to Japan. Making conversation, I said, "Watching you this evening, I would say that you have mixed feelings about returning to Japan."

She laughed and then, suddenly becoming quite serious, said, "Yes, but not for any reason you might think. We have been here almost five years and I'm homesick and can hardly wait to get home. But when I came here I had only one child. Now I have four. How am I going to face my friends at home?"

I looked at her so blankly that she continued, "You are not understanding me, are you? What I mean is that I could have returned happily with two children or maybe even three. But with four children no one will be able to understand — a family this size is really against public opinion."

And it is. For years the Japanese government, prodded on by an aggressive press which found that the subject sold newspapers, has made population control a major preoccupation of the people. Now in all levels of this generation's society it is accepted as unpatriotic not to practice family limitation.

How different in the backward nations!

In 1965 Senator Robert F. Kennedy, who at this writing has nine children, exuberantly shouted to a crowd in the highlands of Peru, "I challenge any of you to produce more children than I have." [53]

They cheered him in Catholic Latin America. In Japan he might well have drawn an official rebuke.

*The Government of Japan Has Firmly Supported Population Control.*

Before one develops any hope that a population control method will be effective in a given country, he should recognize the importance for total and aggressive backing from the government there. It is true that government attitudes are changing in this respect in some places, but not fast enough to give an impact in the next ten years.

Relevant also is the widespread belief among certain political leaders that the power of a country is determined by the size of its population. Some observers have noted that the most active opposition to birth control in Latin America is not the Catholic Church but the left-wingers who claim that birth control programs will castrate their nation's hope for power.

What leader of a hungry nation does not now use the population growth in his country to argue on behalf of the need for new markets, for more foreign aid, to justify educational and medical programs and expensive industrialization — and more P.L. 480 food shipments? Losing a war as Japan did, and thus being forced to turn inward to its own resources, is a dilemma the leaders of these other nations have not experienced.

Of course, it is today politically advantageous for the new governments of the new nations to blame their backwardness on the economic and metropole-centered policies of their former rulers. Now that they have thrown off colonialism (usually by nothing more than an intensive propaganda form of agitation), the leaders feel obliged to shout that paradise has arrived. To say that national problems now stem mostly from too many people having too few resources is to deny to colonialism its proper damnation.

Such was clearly the case when in December 1965 I attended the organizational meeting of the Committee on the World Food Crisis. The press that week had carried daily stories of imminent famine in India. President Johnson had just announced a stepped-up food shipment program to that subcontinent. Studies were under way to expand the Indian port facilities to receive these rush shipments. There was an atmosphere of pending calamity in the room of this committee, engendered by the dismal statistics presented by earlier non-Indian speakers.

Then, in contrast, K. S. Sundara Rajan, Economic Minister of the Indian Embassy and Executive Director for India of the World Bank, rose to speak. The grave food situation in India, he said, was due to having "the worst drought in the last 100 years" (something, obviously, for which the Indians themselves could not be blamed). Then he added, "The average Indian in 1965 is better fed than he was 20 or 30 years ago." (In other words, better fed than under British colonialism.) Although Rajan acknowledged that the food from the United States (which was then shipping 20 per cent of its entire wheat production to India, mostly as P.L. 480 Food) was helpful "in keeping prices stable and removing under-nutrition, . . . much the greatest part of the increased food supplies came from our own production. . . . With great efforts we stepped up the production of our food grains . . . in 1950 and 1951." [54] (That is, after the British were gone; these dates, in any case, are rather meaningless in the present crisis, fifteen years later.)

With such statements still coming from high Indian officials, how can one expect population control to be taken seriously in Delhi and by the Indian public?

*Japan Is Not under the Influence of the Catholic Church.*

The press now often points to changes that may be developing within the Catholic Church with respect to many of its formerly rigid beliefs and traditions. Even concerning the Catholic Church's prohibition against artificial birth control it is pointed out that a large proportion of Catholics do not obey. For instance, 80 per cent of all United States Catholic couples married ten years or longer use some form of artificial birth control.[55] Studies also show that in no society in the world are there any significant differences in the attitude toward family planning between the Catholics and their neighbors, whether in Puerto Rico where the Catholics are in the majority or in Jamaica where they are in the minority or in Lebanon where they are evenly balanced.[56]

But the official Catholic position is quite different. Rev. Dexter L. Hanley of the Jesuits testified before the Senate Committee on Government Operations in August 1965, saying: "I affirm what is already well-known — that according to the theological, moral and authoritative pronouncements of the Catholic Church, the only morally acceptable form of voluntary family regulation is through continence, either total or periodic." [57]

Is there a reader of this book who believes such a practice of continence will have any effect on world population growth?

Thus, the problem is not the Catholic laity but the restraining hand of their church in the halls of government.

The former director of the United Nations World Health Organization (WHO), Brock Chisholm, has written:

> No person can get anywhere in any agency of the United Nations or in any of its committees or commissions, who tries to talk frankly about population problems and their solution. The Population Commission . . . makes terrifying reports every year but it does not make any constructive recommendations because it is not allowed to. Every committee . . . is under the influence of the Roman Catholic Church — and no delegate from the United States, from Canada, from France, from Britain or any of many other countries is in a position where he can even begin to defy that taboo.
>
> I've seen it done. Once when an innocent proposal had been made by the chief delegate from Norway to the effect that the World Health Organization should set up a medical committee to study the medical aspects of population problems, representatives of six governments, chiefs of delegations, immediately got up and said that if this question were even discussed their governments might have to withdraw from the World Health Organization.[58]

Chisholm made this statement in 1959. In 1966 the ban against involvement in population control within the United Nations was still in force: "The World Health Organization refused today to assume international leadership in developing family planning as an answer to the population explosion. . . . The birth-control issue once threatened to disrupt the 18-year old agency because the predominantly Roman Catholic member states opposed its even being raised. It was not until last year that the Assembly approved for the first time some action in the field . . . [but] it was carefully stipulated that this was not to 'involve operational activities.'"[59] Opposition to WHO action in this field was led by France, supported by Argentina, Austria, Belgium, Brazil and Mexico.

"The 30-nation executive board of the United Nations Children's Fund, at its annual meeting early this month in Addis Ababa, voted to defer action on the recommendations of the UNICEF director general that UNICEF consider government requests for assistance in family-planning programs. The recommendations specifically excluded the furnishing of birth-control devices or advice. A varied bloc of nations, led by the Soviet Union and predominantly Roman Catholic countries in Latin America, opposed the director general's report." [60]

"Nowhere [in Mexico] is the rate of population growth less than 3 per cent and in some northern states it is 4 per cent or more. Nowhere are any practical steps to limit this growth discernible. When the question was broached, officials of all types took shelter behind a stock answer: 'We are a Catholic country.' " [61] The citizens of Mexico will for a surety live up to current predictions of an 80,000,000 population in 1987 as compared to 40,000,000 today.[62]

As of this writing press reports from Rome indicate that the current study by the Catholic Church of the problem of birth control may alter its position and sanction certain contraceptives, especially, it is rumored, the use of the Pill. Even if this change is allowed, it will take many years for the lower clergy throughout the world to cease at least passive opposition and to support the programs. Or so it has been with some of the other changes initiated at Rome.

In any case, it seems highly doubtful that the Catholic Church, in spite of its other modernizing changes, will cease active opposition to overall population control in the hungry nations, opposition to the IUD, opposition to legalized abortion, opposition to sterilization. In such areas as Latin America this church's dictum is the major, usually invincible, barrier. Other non-Catholic areas are affected by the same barrier as it prevents or hinders action in the American AID programs, in the Peace Corps, and, of course, in all agencies of the United Nations.

But not in Japan.

Japan is indeed an important case study with respect to population control. It is indeed the pioneer that shows how the birth rate of any nation can be cut in half within a decade.

The tragedy is that no government in any one of the hungry, soon-to-be-starving nations is physically capable or psychologically prepared to duplicate the factors that were responsible for Japan's success.

As the perfect illustration of this whole problem I reprint in full a press dispatch I noticed on an inside page of the morning newspaper:

With four out of 10 of her people under 15 years of age, Turkey is preparing to undertake a program of family planning.

Reducing Turkey's annual population increase of 2.5 per cent — one of the highest in the world — has become an economic necessity. Turkey's population will more than double in 30 years unless the rate is reduced. The rate in the United States is 1.6 per cent.

The vast population growth has slowed economic progress. Heavily burdened with more than $2 billion in foreign debts and a foreign trade deficit above $146 million, Turkey has 1.25 million more mouths to feed than it had two years ago.

Despite more new schools, the illiteracy rate is on the increase. Unemployment is rife and there is an acute housing shortage.

Dr. Nusret Fisek, director general of the Ministry of Health, says a successful program of family planning is "absolutely imperative." The program calls for free provision, through the social health system, of intrauterine loops, devices about the size of a 50-cent piece that have an excellent record of preventing conception. The Government will also supply pills that control ovulation for a token charge of 33 to 55 cents a month.[63]

Here, in a nutshell, is reflected the dilemma of the undeveloped world. Only now is Turkey "preparing to undertake a program of family planning." Not fifteen years ago. Not ten years ago. Only now. In the last two years Turkey's population increased by 1,250,-000. The population will double in thirty years. The nation is overwhelmed by foreign debt payments and an unfavorable trade balance; how will it finance purchases of food from abroad except through charity from other nations?

The world must make room for a billion people to be added to the world's population over the next 15 years. This fact in itself is significant. But even more significant, fully four-fifths of this total will be added in the food-short, less developed regions — regions where the fertility of the people is already outstripping the fertility of the soil.[64]

The United Nations loves to promote mouth-watering terms like the Geophysical Decade, the Year of the Quiet Sun, the International Cooperation Year, etc. What the United Nations should

# GROWTH IN WORLD'S POPULATION
# VS. INCREASE IN ARABLE LAND

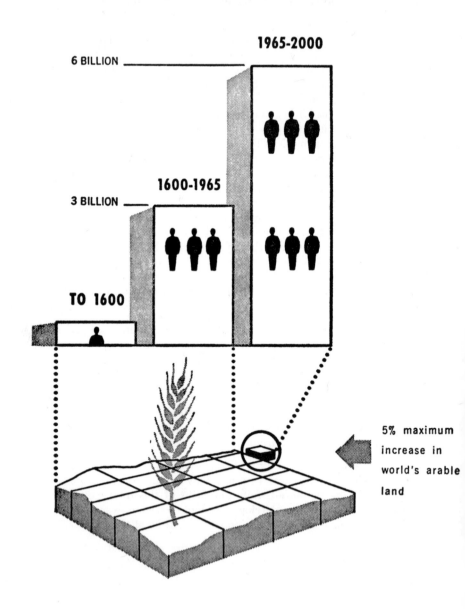

1965-2000

6 BILLION

1600-1965

3 BILLION

TO 1600

5% maximum increase in world's arable land

do — and the very thought of it would cringe the stoutest heart at the Delegates' Bar — is to promote a Childless Year.[65]

Malthus, the economist, summarized it as graphically as is possible: population will increase in geometrical progression — 1, 2, 4, 8, 16, 32 — but food will increase in arithmetical progression — 1, 2, 3, 4, 5, 6.

Let the diagram on page 38 [66] sink deep into your mind. The key part of it, just so you do not miss it, is the little black block in the circle indicating the additional land that is expected to grow the additional food that is not going to feed the multitudes.

# 2

## *Today Hungry Nations, Tomorrow Starving Nations*

In college I took two courses in statistics. The first I almost understood. The second was incomprehensible, but Professor Josiah Livermore closed the course with a piece of advice I have applied profitably many times: "When the statistics go against your reasoned judgment, throw the statistics out the window!"

I applied this precept when I doubted the optimistic statements and figures in an address given by Secretary of Agriculture Orville L. Freeman at the United Nations Food and Agriculture Organization (FAO) in Rome at the end of 1965. He said: "I should like to unfurl the banner of hope, a hope that arises because it now seems possible to win the war against hunger within the next ten or twenty years. . . . My optimism arises out of the conclusions of a study [which] reveals the startling fact that some newly developing countries are already increasing their agricultural production at rates far higher than those ever achieved by the highly developed nations — including my own." [1] The Secretary then quoted in support of his optimism parts of a statistical study just released by his department, *Changes in Agriculture in 26 Developing Nations 1948-1963*, published in late 1965. [2]

Wide publicity was given to the Secretary's speech; editorials and other comment conveyed the assurance that there is little to worry about regarding food shortages in these nations.

However, when I reviewed this same study, its conclusion did not, in my opinion, ring true. Because my own observations in many of the countries had been exactly the opposite of the statements in this study, I made inquiry concerning its background. It turned out that despite its title dates of "1948-1963" the data did not go beyond 1962, and the figures were merely *averaged out* for the full period 1948-1962. When I broke down these same figures by year, it developed that nearly all the increases in production had occurred from 1948 to 1955. After 1955 per capita production has decreased steadily, thus verifying the trends I had myself noted on the spot — a situation which might have been apparent if the study had indeed included data from 1962 up to the time Freeman addressed the FAO Conference in 1965.

"When the statistics go against your reasoned judgment, throw the statistics out the window!"

Therefore, based on my reasoned judgment, and despite the optimistic statements of Mr. Freeman, whom I greatly admire as one of the most effective officials in Washington, I state flatly that the hungry world will not be able to feed itself ten years from now. If twenty years from now it feeds itself, it will do so either because some now unknown method of improved food production has been discovered (most unlikely!) or because the population has been drastically reduced by famine or war. My statement is based not only on my own experiences and observations abroad but also on the statistics of:

(1) the somersault of export-import food shipments;
(2) the lagging productive capacity of the land in the hungry nations; and
(3) the extent of hunger in the world today.

## *The Somersault of Export-Import Food Shipments*

Prior to World War II today's hungry nations were exporters of grain. By the 1950's they had become importers!

In the 1930's Latin America exported more grain than the United States and Canada combined. In 1949 Latin America became a grain importer!

It is not only the sheer bulk size of this change that has caught the world off guard and has left the leaders floundering for remedies. It is the speed at which this somersault has taken place.

The citizens of the nations which so suddenly lost their capacity to export food (and, therefore, had to import it) often did not realize what was happening. Indeed, it took the publication of a report in 1963 (*Man, Land and Food*) by the perceptive young Department of Agriculture economist, Lester R. Brown, to bring this first to the attention of American officials.

Those concerned with calculating the balance of payments in these nations were, however, well aware of the catastrophe that was occurring to their cash flow. If there had been any way, any way whatever, within the bounds of their knowledge and ability to stop this outflow of their cash, the governments would have acted. I hedged, it will be noted, by saying "within the bounds of their knowledge and ability." Now, in retrospect, many officials realize that their surge to create artificial industrialization and their parallel neglect of agriculture were wrong. Wrong, too, were the half-hearted efforts given to agriculture by the aid-givers in contrast to their excessive emphasis on projects which do not increase food production: hospitals, highways, drinking water, urban housing, etc.

Since the war, the United States and Canada have become the principal food exporters. Both have always been important exporters of agricultural products, but only recently have they come to dominate the international market so strikingly. Today's situation is due partly to their own agricultural expansions based on the application of new scientific knowledge. Yet it is also due to the withdrawal of other producers from the international markets; in a sense, our farmers have simply filled the vacuum resulting from this unexpected, sudden somersault within the former exporting nations. The completeness of the somersault is seen in the graph.[3]

The former, prewar suppliers of foodstuffs for the international markets have, one by one, been forced to use their former excess food supplies to feed their own growing populations. Now they must import more than they export.

Before the war I was stationed in the Consulate General at Batavia, Netherlands Indies (now Djakarta, Indonesia). One of my jobs was to prepare periodic reports for the Department of Agriculture on local export crops, such as citronella, rubber, tea, etc. The crop that interested me most was copra. Most of the others were grown on large company-owned estates. Copra, a source of edible oil from coconuts, usually was raised on peasant-type holdings. The

# SOMERSAULT IN NET FLOW OF WORLD GRAIN

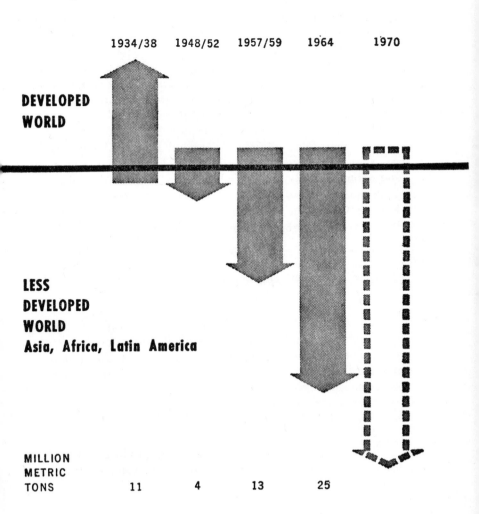

|  | 1934/38 | 1948/52 | 1957/59 | 1964 | 1970 |
|---|---|---|---|---|---|

**DEVELOPED WORLD**

**LESS DEVELOPED WORLD**
Asia, Africa, Latin America

| MILLION METRIC TONS | 11 | 4 | 13 | 25 | |

world price was deep in the doldrums and, as I went around the archipelago, it was easy to translate this directly into how it affected the beautiful small islands where the coconut trees were the only evidence of economic activity. The islands were so beautiful with the elegant palms and the gentle life of the people; to the casual visitor it all seemed idyllic. Actually, the good life on the palm-rimmed holdings rose and fell with the export price of their copra. The Netherlands Indies was a major prewar supplier of copra on the world market. Indonesia, in contrast, exported in 1963 only one-fifth of the amount of 1938,[4] although the total amount grown was greater than the crop of 1938.[5] Various excuses are offered: one, that during the struggle for independence much of the rebel activity centered in the copra-producing areas (although that was a decade and a half ago), and another, the turmoil brought on by Sukarno's socialistic controls over the local economy. The *real* reason: the increased population is consuming the other four-fifths that formerly was exported.

This copra is one example out of many from the hungry nations concerning changes in the ratio of food production versus consumption. Multiply this example a thousandfold with similar illustrations of wheat in India, soybeans in China, corn in Nicaragua, beans in Chile. The reasons for the post-World War II somersault in the export-import food shipments then become clear.

## The Lagging Productive Capacity of the Land in the Hungry Nations

Up until 1957-1959 the world as a whole was doing pretty well regarding food. It was, in fact, increasing its agricultural production somewhat faster than the number of mouths to be fed. It managed this largely by putting new land into production throughout the undeveloped countries.

But then the increases began to falter. By 1958 these countries had run out of new land which they could farm.

The stork had passed the plow.

The undeveloped nations were failing to produce enough food for their expanding populations. Imports of food began. Something like half the net regional imports of the hungry nations were required to offset the decline in per capita output.[6]

Beginning in 1963 FAO has issued regular statements that the world's population is growing one per cent faster than its food production.

B. R. Sen, Director General of FAO, stated in a letter he sent in 1965 to Ministers and Secretaries of Agriculture throughout the world:

> While a small movement up or down in a single year in food production per head may not be significant, we are now facing something far more serious. The stark fact is that it is now no less than seven years since there was any appreciable increase in food production per head of the world's population, seven very lean years for the developing countries. The outlook is alarming. In some of the most heavily populated areas the outbreak of serious famines within the next five to ten years cannot be excluded.[7]

Then FAO disclosed that there had been *no* increase in agricultural production in 1966 even though the world population had grown that year by 70 million. In fact, Latin American, African and Asian food production had actually dropped so that there was 4 to 5 per cent less food available for each person in those hungry areas than there was the previous year. Sen summed up the situation by saying, "The world food situation is now more precarious than at any time since the period of acute shortage immediately after the Second World War." [8]

There are several ways to verify the failure of agriculture to produce food in pace with the expanding population.

For instance, if it is true that per capita production of food is decreasing one can expect the law of supply and demand to push up food prices. A recent study shows that this is exactly what is happening. Almost half of the developing nations for which data are available show food prices rising faster than the cost of living — as normally occurs when per capita food production falls.[9]

When food prices go up, then one must also expect that submarginal land, which formerly was unprofitable to farm, will be brought into production. Again there is ample evidence this has happened throughout much of the world. Look at per acre yields. Not only is agricultural production in the hungry nations falling on a per capita basis; in some it is falling on a per acre basis. Recent data developed by the Department of Agriculture reveal that corn yields per acre in Colombia, Venezuela and Ecuador were higher in 1955-1959 than in 1961-1963. In Brazil both wheat and corn per acre yields were higher in 1935-1939 than in 1955-1960. Guatemala had the greatest drop, with yields falling from 15.7 bushels to the acre in 1939 to less than 12 in 1962.[10]

The fall in acre yields in these examples may soon become more and more evident throughout the undeveloped world. Land has been put into producton which simply lacks the qualities needed to *maintain* production. The rising cost of food combined with the population pressures on the land have pushed farmers farther and farther up the hillsides and farther and farther out into the jungle. They are now tilling land which should never have been farmed. This land may be able to raise a few crops successfully, but then the yields fall off because its low quality will not permit sustained production — at least not until new cultural techniques are evolved for that land through years of research.

Since World War II four-fifths of the increase in agricultural production in the undeveloped countries has resulted not from the use of fertilizers or other new twentieth-century technology, but from putting into production land which hitherto was unused. It was nothing more than extending traditional farming methods into submarginal land.[11] By 1958 virtually all of the unused, submarginal land which could be brought into production even on a forced, substandard basis was being farmed. Thus, with no new technology and no new marginal land available the race between food production and mouths to be fed — the race which until then agriculture had at least been keeping up with — now began to be lost.

Throughout much of the tropics the subsistence farmer traditionally uses a slash-and-burn technique. Every three or four years he abandons his land, moves to another plot, cuts down the brush, lets this dry and then burns it. Then he plants his corn or cassava or platanos or whatever is the staff of life in his region. The land that he moves away from is left fallow to grow weeds and brush until he returns to use it again. In the good old days he did not return to it for seven, eight or more years. Now, however, with more people pressuring to live off the land he must use the plots more and more frequently. Land that used to rest eight years between cultivations is now idle only six years. This two-year difference results in lower yields.

Whether or not one is skeptical of the accuracy of the official statistics from the undeveloped countries, the projected trends cannot be doubted. These trends add up to one conclusion:

The hungry nations have lost the capacity to feed themselves from the land available to them.

Nowhere is this more pronounced than in the tropics, where food production per capita is falling most rapidly. However, the urgency of the world food crisis stems from a few areas peripheral to the tropics where the sheer mass of humanity, as in Pakistan, northern India and China, makes any drop in per capita production a frightening figure.

Egypt is the gaudy example of the land/population treadmill on which the hungry nations now find themselves. The nub of Egypt's exploding crisis is illustrated by the steadily increasing percentage of its agricultural imports in relation to total imports, as follows:[12]

|  | *Per Cent of Total Agricultural Imports* |
|---|---|
| 1954 | 17.8 |
| 1960 | 25.2 |
| 1965 | 30.2 |

*Excluded* from these percentages is the major item of P.L. 480 shipments from the United States which, since 1954, have amounted to considerably more than a billion dollars.[13]

In 1947 Egypt's population was increasing at a rate of 340,000 additional mouths a year. This was a modest number compared to 1964 when Nasser announced his country had increased that year by 800,000 "little Egyptians." "Bless them!" he said, "but we cannot go on this way."

Egypt's farmable land, lying between the desert and the Nile, is more firmly circumscribed than any other country's. Nasser's solution to the need for increased food production is the new Aswan Dam. It is planned that this dam will increase the arable land by one-third. It is to be the great national victory over hunger. It is to bring Egypt in one jump, in one decade, from the Middle Ages into the twentieth century.

Alas! During the ten-year period of construction Egypt's population itself will have increased by one-third.

The increased food and industrial resources resulting from the enormous financial ($1.5 billion) and physical effort represented by the dam will only balance out against the population growth. Egypt will be no better fed after the dam is finished than when construction began.[14]

The one benefit that the Aswan Dam might have bought has been thrown away — time. If Nasser had started ten years ago an energetic population control program, effective results could well be under way ten or fifteen years from now. And he might have started an agricultural research program ten years ago to find out how to use more efficiently the present land and the new Aswan Dam land. He failed to do either of these things.

"Not until February [1966], under the stimulus of outside encouragement, did Egypt formally begin a nationwide campaign to check its rampant population rise"[15] (although it had officially endorsed birth control in 1962). Only now have the newspapers begun to campaign against large families with such things as a cartoon picturing two babies in a hospital nursery, with one saying, "What in God's name are you doing coming to this overcrowded country!"[16] Significantly, the campaign was not pushed into an action program by the Egyptian leadership; they remained passive and apparently disinterested in the face of the mounting statistics.[17] Only when free money was offered by such foreign organizations as the Ford Foundation and the Population Council, and by the United States and Swedish governments, were Nasser and the rest of the leadership willing to work actively for population control.

The interplay of exploding population and bogged-down food production is highlighted in Egypt for all to see and comprehend, because here the agricultural land is absolutely fixed. In Egypt the issue rings forth clear as a bell: cut down the population growth or increase food production per acre. Egypt is doing neither. The Aswan Dam is only a delusion of progress; its new lands will be farmed in the same old ways by the same old fellahins procreating as always without effective official support to curtail family size.

When a country has no new land into which to expand, it becomes dependent upon food from foreign countries. Egypt's precarious, deteriorating position is a clear example. Look at that country's growing imports for wheat and wheat flour (including P. L. 480 shipments) :[18]

|  | Metric Tons |
|---|---|
| 1954 | 58,000 |
| 1960 | 1,175,000 |
| 1962 | 1,370,000 |
| 1964 | 1,586,000 |
| 1965 | 1,840,000 |

## The Extent of Hunger in the World Today

Many observers claim that the somersault from exporter to importer is largely the result of people in those countries eating better today than before World War II. For instance, here is a statement in the same Department of Agriculture study to which I referred earlier, the one that the Secretary of Agriculture quoted so optimistically. The study states that high incomes, especially in the cities, are increasing the demand for food in most of the world's less developed countries. "Consequently, for the first time in its history, India's food shortage is not the result of crop failures and declining per capita food output, but of the increased capacity of its people to buy the food they need." [19]

Such reasoning is false, I believe, and the proof is the increasing hunger so openly evident throughout these same nations. Whatever upgrading of diet may have taken place has occurred primarily among a few favored sectors of the populace, not across the board. This change does not extend beyond a limited group in the cities.

"I'm hungry" is an elusive phrase to pin down. Obviously, it is said in different tones by the American teen-ager than by the Calcutta slum dweller. Even the nutritionists with all their charts and involuted terms cannot really draw a clean-cut line between malnutrition and starvation.

How big an area must be affected before it can be classified as famine-stricken?

What percentage of the population of the undeveloped nations should be called suffering from malnutrition?

The tourist in Lima, Singapore and Dakar possibly sees no malnutrition around him at all — if, that is, he stays in the well-to-do heart of the city, nor will he in the similar heart of Philadelphia, Savannah or London.

Perhaps when a man keels over and collapses from lack of food, then that can be accepted as the dividing line between malnutrition and starvation. Perhaps when whole families and communities keel over, then it can be called a famine. All this, unfortunately, is bad scientific terminology.

An added complication is that it is mighty hard actually to starve to death. "Starvation has to be extreme and of long duration to cause death *if adequate medical care is provided.* With the increase in quantity and quality of medical care, it seems likely that deaths from a given level of mass starvation would be much less today in a given country than would have been the case 20 or 30 years ago." [20]

If, however, I am going to predict in these pages what will happen in the world as food becomes scarcer, I ought to be able to say when a man is hungry, when he is suffering from malnutrition, when he is dying from starvation. Unfortunately, I cannot.

I like best the simple explanation of Boyd Orr, Nobel Laureate and former head of FAO: "All I have learned about calories, proteins, carbohydrates, trace-elements, vitamins and enzymes is this: If people are hungry, they need food. If they are ill-nourished they need good food." [21]

The most commonly used criterion to measure a nation's dietary level is a measuring of its food energy supply in terms of calories. Caloric requirements vary on the basis of the size of the man (or woman), the work he does and the climate in which he lives. Nevertheless, accepted estimates for calorie consumption have been established and the Department of Agriculture has devised from them a so-called world food budget. This shows:

"The share of the population . . . living in countries with average energy (calorie) supply levels below the minimum recommended was 92% for Asia, 38% for Africa and 29% for Latin

America." This amounts to 79 per cent of the population in the underdeveloped regions or 56 per cent of the entire world.[22]

So three out of every four people in the developing world do not have enough calories!

A new factor regarding calories has now arisen. Recent research indicates the likelihood of a 5 to 10 per cent error in all calorie statistics regarding the tropics. Until now it has been the standard practice to state that people need less food in the tropics than in the temperate zones. Thus, FAO in its calculations recommends a 5 per cent decrease in food requirements for every 10-degree increase in environmental temperatures. However, tests by the United States Army Medical Research and Nutrition Laboratory at Denver have shown that just the opposite appears to be true.[23] This means, then, that the hotter the weather the *more* food the individual needs to perform his work. Since the hungry nations are nearly all in the tropics, it would appear as if the FAO figures should be increased by another 50 million people suffering from malnutrition — give or take a dozen million people!

During the last war there were two long sieges that ranked with just about any of the famous ones of history. One was in Leningrad and the other in Malta. In both the populace for months at a time was reduced to the last extremity before actual starvation, yet in both the fighting spirit of the people never flagged.

I lived in Moscow shortly after the Leningrad siege was broken and the Germans pushed back, and I also lived in Malta after the war. The constant stories I heard about both sieges seemed always to be centered not on the lack of food but on the great excitement whenever a load of food would somehow manage to break through the enemy lines. In Leningrad the Russians were able to keep open for one winter a workable road across a frozen lake. In Malta the successive relief convoys would be terribly battered but usually at least one ship would make it. In both places the citizens were surely suffering from malnutrition for prolonged periods, but the elated spirits of wartime action apparently counteracted the adverse physical and psychological factors. Always there was hope that next week, next month, there would be enough food.

There is no such hope among today's sufferers from malnutrition. Automatically, that makes them more liable to succumb to every passing germ or merely to waste themselves away in apathy.

The graph on page 53 illustrates that while today the gap is indeed wide between the food production of these hungry nations and their food demands, tomorrow the gap will be wider.[24]

If this graph seems unrealistic, I counter with another fearsome factor. Who has not looked in awe at the teen-ager who, having just eaten two hamburgers and a malted milk on his way home from school, settles down to a full-course meal with his family? Who eats more than teen-agers? Actually, no one. And 42 per cent of the people in the undeveloped world are under the age of fifteen.[25] Most of these children, in contrast to earlier years, will be kept alive by the new public health facilities and will grow up to adult age.

The graph[26] on page 54 shows how quickly the demand for food accelerates as a child five years old, requiring only 1600 calories a day, skyrockets to the fifteen-year-old needing 2800. If the undeveloped world cannot now feed itself, consider the difficulty when today's huge child population reaches its late teens.

Just as the food requirements of a child shoot up with the years, so will the food requirements of the hungry nations. These will skyrocket *faster* than the simple population growth percentages.

Of course, calories are only part of the health picture. Necessary to man's energy is protein, which is an indicator of the "quality" of the diet available. Here again, over half the world lives in countries which do not have a protein intake that meets minimum acceptable standards. Also, fats are needed by man. "90 per cent of Asia's population is included in those countries with fat intake below the [recommended] standards." [27]

Hunger in its many forms, whether protein deficiency or fat deficiency or just plain empty belly, is an affliction, a scourge, a plague from one continent to another.

The crisis of population explosion versus static agriculture is indeed formed. The nations of the undeveloped world are no longer grain exporters, they are grain importers. There is no more unused land to bring into cultivation; even the deficient marginal land is by now in use. Hunger is rampant throughout country after country, continent after continent around the undeveloped belt of the

# DATA FOR
## LATIN AMERICA, FAR EAST, NEAR EAST AND AFRICA
### (The Hungry Nations)

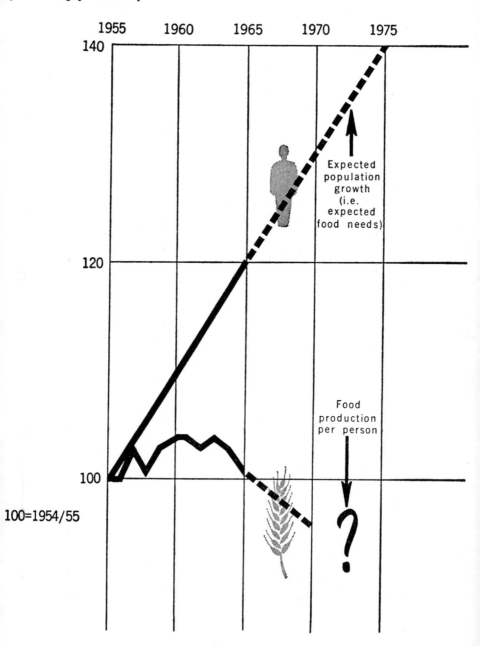

1955 1960 1965 1970 1975

140

Expected
population
growth
(i.e.
expected
food needs)

120

Food
production
per person

100

100=1954/55

?

# CALORIE REQUIREMENTS AT DIFFERENT AGE LEVELS

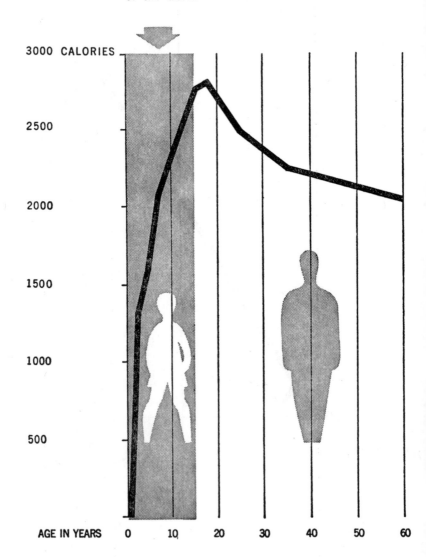

Under 15 years –
Age group of HALF the people
now living
in the hungry nations
of the world

3000 CALORIES

2500

2000

1500

1000

500

AGE IN YEARS      0        10        20        30        40        50        60

tropics and subtropics. Today's crisis can move in only one direction — toward catastrophe.

Today hungry nations; tomorrow starving nations.

## *1975 — The Hunger Becomes Famine*

In a 1966 seminar I attended at the Hudson Institute one of the speakers said: "People who publish population figures are propagandists. They like the extreme projections. Everyone else believes population figures will decrease sharply within a generation."

Maybe so. I hope so. Yet even a generation is too short a lead time if — always that "if" — the population figures do, after all, "decrease sharply."

For the short, ten-year span from 1965 to 1975 United Nations projections for population growth show how much additional food will be required.[28]

FUTURE FOOD REQUIREMENTS OF THE HUNGRY WORLD

|  | Population at Current Rates of Growth | | Additional Food Production Needed Within Ten Years |
|---|---|---|---|
|  | 1965 | 1975 |  |
| East Asia | 867 million | 1.04 billion | 20% |
| South Asia | 975 million | 1.25 billion | 28% |
| Africa | 311 million | 404 million | 30% |
| Latin America | 248 million | 335 million | 35% |
| TOTAL | 2.4 billion | 3.0 billion | 26% |

Thus, simply to maintain today's inadequate dietary levels, the hungry nations must increase their production within a single decade by 26 per cent.

For reasons covered in the next chapter, agricultural increases such as these cannot be attained by 1975. Since this is so then the diets of these nations must become considerably less than even today's level of malnutrition.

The end result for each of the affected nations will be the constant threat of catastrophe. Whenever there is too much or too little rain, whenever spring comes late or the harvest is wet, whenever civil unrest delays the plantings, whenever *anything* reduces the yield, then a portion of the population will slip over into the chasm of starvation.

"Famine isn't like a satellite count-down; you don't say, 'Three-two-one, it's here!' What happens is like the New York water shortage: it develops slowly; experts wring hands; public pays no attention; then, suddenly, it's headlined. That's what's happening in world food." [29] We cannot say precisely what it takes to starve a man to death. It is clear, however, that if the undeveloped world is not feeding itself today, it will feed itself even less well tomorrow.

The Swedish economist Gunnar Myrdal sees a "world calamity" in "five or ten years." [30]

Chester Bowles, Ambassador to India, says that the approaching world famine threatens to be "the most colossal catastrophe in history." [81]

Thomas M. Ware, testifying before a Senate committee, said, "Very few grasp the magnitude of the danger that confronts us." [32]

Dr. Raymond Ewell: "The world is on the threshold of the biggest famine in history. If present trends continue, it seems likely that famine will reach serious proportions in India, Pakistan and China in the early 1970's. . . . Such a famine will be of massive proportions affecting hundreds of millions." [83]

I agree with these forecasters, but I must be more specific — and in Chapter 5, I give reasons for choosing an actual year.

1975 will be a crucial year in the world, crucial because the world food shortage will then dominate the headlines and the results will be in full view. The present downward trends cannot be reversed, nor can they be dusted under the carpet. Those who say there are too many variables in the future to forecast food deficits ignore the present trends.

## India Is the Bellwether

India is the case in point. It is the bellwether that shows the path which the others, like sheep going to the slaughter, are following. The hungry nation that today refuses to heed India's history will be condemned to relive it. "The future of mankind is now being ground out in India. If no solution [is found], all the world will live as India does now." [34]

The present food crisis of India was predicted officially in 1959. In that year the Indian government, with the help of the Ford Foundation, issued a report which accurately forecast, it is now painfully realized, the serious gap that would arise by 1965-1966 between food stocks and consumption needs. Its warning of trouble and civil tensions as a result of this gap was explicit: "We have reached the inescapable conclusion that a rapid increase in production of food is India's primary problem in achieving human welfare, social justice and democracy over the next seven years. . . . The entire nation must be made aware of the impending food crisis and steps must be taken to meet it. . . . The statement has been made by Indian leaders that if the food problem is to be solved the work must be placed on a 'war footing.' . . . But an effective crusade involves more than plans. . . . 'Business as usual' will not achieve the food production targets." [35]

The Indian leadership did not do this. "Business as usual" continued with the government's emphasis on industry, its downgrading of agriculture and its insistence on socialistic controls throughout the economy.

Many of the hungry nations are, to be sure, more preoccupied today with their agricultural problems than they, or India, were eight years ago, but there is still seldom any real sense of urgency. Thus, today's troubles in India will soon become the fate of others.

India's policies on the use of fertilizers is probably as good a single example as can be found of what I mean by no real sense of urgency. India uses an amazingly small amount of fertilizer, only about three pounds of nutrients to the acre (compared with 300 in Japan, 180 in Taiwan and 100 in Korea).[36] Yet, in spite of the generally recognized need to increase the national manufacture of fertilizers, the socialistic Indian government has restricted the production of fertilizer by private industries while not making any real effort to develop the government's own small production. The government "has restricted private sales of nitrogenous fertilizer and then boosted the price of fertilizer through co-op channels in order to protect high-cost government plants; and it has not either permitted or constructed a distribution sysem to get fertilizer to the farmers when they need it on credit terms that are possible for the majority of farmers." [37] This favoring of government-owned fertilizer plants and harassing of privately owned plants to the detriment of the nation does, incidentally, seem to be an illustrative example of a typical weakness of the typical socialist government in the undeveloped world. It is a pertinent example of how difficult it will be for these governments to plan clearly and coolheadedly in order to prepare for the future famines.

Since the British left, India has tied its dreams to industrialization. One reason this was possible was that the country did make significant increases in agricultural production during the 1950's (a 46 per cent increase from 1951 to 1961 — most of which resulted from putting new land into production),[38] and thus was not forced to think in terms of food. But then the agricultural facts of life caught up with India. For three years (1962-1964) "food-grain production in India . . . remained virtua¹ly stagnant while population during the same period . . . increased by about 33 million people." The result was a sharp rise in food-grain prices.[39] India's confidence faltered, but only for a moment. The Lord smiled again (in the form of good weather) in the crop year of 1964-1965 and India increased its agricultural production 10 per cent.[40] Confidence was great. Yet even this good production year was not enough. Whereas the Third Five Year Plan (1960-1965) had projected a production of 119 million tons of food grains (more than enough to feed the population), only 80 million tons were produced. Seven million tons of food had to be imported. Grain prices rose 30 to 40 per cent as supplies failed to meet the nation's needs.[41] When shipments were delayed a few weeks by a longshoremen's strike in the United States, food riots erupted. India was living literally "from ship to mouth."

The 1959 prediction of a food crisis in 1966, to which I referred earlier, and the Indian government's failure to heed its own warning underscore the fact that predicting civil troubles as a result of food shortages can be done with considerable accuracy. Those who found the Indian food crisis of 1966 a startling awakening may not have seen the 1959 prediction, but by 1964 the headlines clearly showed what was coming.

November 1964: "Storming mobs of angry Indians brought the

southern state of Kerala to the brink of anarchy last week. Driven by hunger and prodded by the Communists, crowds looted shops and warehouses in a frantic search for food. . . . Students raced through the streets challenging the police to 'give us rice or shoot us.' " [42] The central government was able to reroute eighty thousand tons of wheat and rice into the troubled area.[43] This crisis expedient quelled — for a while — the riots which in retrospect are reported to have been caused not by direct, immediate hunger but by anger that the local rice ration had been cut to the bone while a neighboring state received a much larger ration.[44] Either way, the riots were real enough and a portent of times to come.

[The U.S. sent in] stopgap help for India. About $400 million worth of U.S. food — wheat, rice, soybean oil — is to pour into India between now and next June 30 [1965]. The Indians are as usual to pay in rupees, most of which the U.S. will immediately lend back to them. . . . In a sense, a moment of truth is upon India.[45]

Parallel with these sad statistics India came to the end of its financial rope. In 1964 it had debts which required $225 million a year just to service. Most of these debts were owed to Europeans or to the World Bank and default is a matter of time. The American suppliers of food and industrial products were not caught in this bind because they had already been paid directly by the United States government out of tax receipts. In 1964 the United States owned 12 billion rupees ($2.5 billion) derived largely from sale of U.S. food to the Indian government. "More than half the rupees now circulating in India are really owned by the U.S." [46] (by 1966 this was to be estimated at two-thirds!).

In December 1964 the all-India price index for cereal grains was 21.4 per cent higher than in December 1963.[47] The price of beans was 60 per cent higher. India made frantic efforts to procure more food. It arranged for 59,000 tons of rice from Thailand and 35,000 tons from Cambodia. A new year-end amendment of the P.L. 480 agreement provided for an extra 130,000 tons of U.S. corn and 50,000 tons of U.S. rice.[48]

Just the same, by August 1965 India was facing its greatest food crisis since the terrible Bihar famine of 1951. Riots broke out in Kilhapur, near Bombay, when an "Anti-starvation Action Committee" was formed.[49] The Indian government, in an effort to accumulate some wheat and rice reserves, reduced the people's diets from 14.4 ounces of wheat and rice a day to 12 ounces.[50]

By then food was arriving at the rate of two ships a day from the United States. And no other source of food was available. Australia and Canada had committed their wheat stocks to China.[51]

And in September war broke out between Pakistan and India. The war pacified, temporarily, the unrest arising from the food shortages, but also it obviously diverted funds into the army that otherwise might have been used in agricultural development.

By 1974 India will have increased her population by 120 million.[52] India cannot, literally cannot, feed that many more mouths. Even the United States would find it appalling to try and feed that kind of increase in numbers within its own borders within the space of eight years.

Today India totters. Tomorrow: "The most vulnerable countries include India, Pakistan, Communist China, Indonesia, Iran, Turkey, Egypt, Colombia, Peru and several other countries of Latin America. Mass starvation seems likely to hit these countries within five to ten years, or even sooner." [53] The resulting unrest will not erupt simultaneously everywhere. Like India's series of riots and disturbances, each will erupt spasmodically, but the time of quiet between eruptions will grow shorter. "[Some countries] such as Burma, Thailand, the Philippines, Nigeria, Ghana, Chile and others seem to be in relatively good shape food-wise at present, but they all have such high population growth rates that they will be in serious difficulties in a few more years [after 1980]." [54]

Vice-President Humphrey flies to India and announces a $100,-000,000 loan. President Johnson decrees stepped-up food shipments. North Carolina's representative Harold D. Cooley even proposes using the United States Air Force to air-lift food within India.[55] Presumably, this will be enough to save it for 1966 and perhaps for a few years to come. But when the crisis continues, what happens next? For by then other countries will be floundering with India.

Today, India is the first of the hungry nations to stand at the brink of famine and disaster. Being the first, it receives the full bounty of United States food generosity. India is today's handwriting-on-the-wall for the hungry nations in the year of 1975.

"The 'Four Horsemen of the Apocalypse' — pestilence, war, famine and death — continue to stalk the world. Although they may emerge at different times from different doors, the fact remains that they come from the same barn." [56]

The trend of export-import food statistics and the lagging productive capacity of the hungry nations show clearly that hunger is not only here today but is steadily increasing.

By 1975 civil disorder, anarchy, military dictatorships, runaway inflation, transportation breakdowns and chaotic unrest will be the order of the day in many of the hungry nations — all because hunger will turn inexorably into starvation and starvation will become widespread famine.

I opened this chapter by criticizing a 1965 speech of the Secretary of Agriculture as falsely optimistic. It is well to close by quoting from a speech he made a year later which to me seems more realistic.

The encouraging advances in per capita food production recorded in the developing countries during the 1950's have been reversed in many cases during the present decade. . . . Virtually all studies . . . have underestimated increases in the demand for food, largely because of underestimates of population growth, and they have overestimated increases in food production in the developing countries.

If the rate of increase [of wheat imports] over the next decade should even remotely approach that of the decade just ended, world import demand for wheat will far exceed the supply capabilities of the exporting countries. . . . Unless the less developed countries sharply increase their agricultural productivity, and soon, mass famine will take place. Thus more human lives hang in the balance in the race between food and people than have been lost in all the wars of history.[57]

# 3

## *"Something" Will Turn Up to Avert Famine— or Will It?*

"We don't brood over dried-up faucets. We are surrounded by the world's most beautiful scenery and the world's most beautiful women. We have the sea to wash off our worries and the sun to dry our tears." [1]

So speaks Vinicius des Moraes, author of *Black Orpheus*, concerning Rio de Janeiro, a city where the scenery and the sea and the women are indeed gorgeous. The trouble is you don't see them in the despairing slum *favelas*. Rio has generated on a gigantic scale just about every problem of horrendous urbanization and overpopulation and undereating that it is possible to create. It is a case history of everything that is wrong with the modern world. And the sea does *not* wash off the worries and the sun does *not* dry the tears.

The statistics and conclusions of the foregoing chapters are, certainly, lugubrious. Yet human nature tends to shrug off the troubles of the future and says, "Something will turn up. It always has." It is true that man's ingenuity has saved many a crisis, has turned away the scythe of catastrophe many times. It is also true, alack, that there have been plenty of sad disasters where, after all, nothing did turn up to save the people.

In the area of food production there are today many valid ideas in the research laboratories that some day will increase output. Many of the finest research brains are active on this problem. It is discouraging that their efforts are concentrated almost entirely on new techniques for temperate zone agriculture. My own belief is that if the scientists would place an equal effort on applying to the tropics and subtropics the knowledge already available within the developed world, then there might be hope that adequate results could be obtained in time to alleviate the famines. Note that we spend in the United States nearly *one billion* dollars a year on agricultural research but that we allocate only *four million* dollars for research in tropical Latin America,[2] the area with the world's fastest falling rate of per capita food production.

For the hungry nations it is unfortunate, in my opinion, that today the major efforts by the universities and foundations in all countries are directed to *pure*, rather than *applied*, research. Time does not remain for the scientists to bring to conclusion their pure research in that small percentage of projects dealing with food production that turn out successfully, and then for others to make the results practical, and then for businessmen and officials to put the new techniques into mass production, and then finally for everyone combined to get the masses to use the results. I am not against pure research which is, of course, the basis of science; it is just that I wish equal support were being given to the application of today's techniques of temperate zone agriculture for the production of food in the tropics.

Unfortunately, it is the far-out ideas on which the scientists are working (quite a legitimate field for scientific research) that receive excessive prominence not only in learned journals and at international meetings but more especially in mass circulation magazines. The media seem to pounce on each glimmer of news from the laboratories and to inflate it into a story in which the tentative aspects, the unproven aspects, are somehow lost from sight. Hence, the general public as well as the nation's leadership is often misled into false hopes. As good an example as any is a 1966 speech by Congressman Richard T. Hanna of California in the House of Representatives.

He said the world now has the "potential" to feed "ten times the present population of the earth or 30 billion people. . . . Food technology . . . now stands on the frontier of a fantastic new development which can produce protein foods high in quality, low in price and easily distributed." He named three "food frontiers" which can be developed to cut back the present shortage of food: pasteurization of food products by new methods of radiation and high-frequency waves; protein concentrates; and freeze-dry food processing.[3]

These "food frontiers" of which the congressman spoke have, I emphasize, yet to be crossed by science for feeding the hungry world. The time left before the famines and civil unrest is too short a period to carry through those projects which today are in the test tubes. Even with the most ideal conditions of adequate financing, adequate personnel, adequate government support, adequate public understanding, time has run out.

Too little time is an ogre that devours the panaceas of the planners and the hopes of the optimists.

## The Panacea of Synthetic Foods

The chemist can make a strong case for his capability to supply man with most of his necessities. A large portion of man's non-food essentials which formerly were derived from agricultural products are today synthesized. This applies to 99 per cent of the dyes now produced, 52 per cent of the rubber, 25 per cent of all textiles.[4]

Today a serious effort is being made in chemical laboratories to synthesize food.

### Synthesized Proteins and Vitamins

The proteins, the scarcest of all foods, are composed of amino acids. The synthesizing of these acids has for some time been a major effort in many laboratories in the United States and Europe. Yet of the eight essential amino acids which must be supplied by one's diet only methionine is produced today on a commercial scale. Lysine has been chemically synthesized by the Hollanders, but it remains a costly product and its economical use for humans has not yet been determined [5] — although lysine, produced by a fermentation process, is now used in some "high protein" breads and breakfast foods in the United States.[6] The other six amino acids are still under laboratory investigation.[7] If an all-out effort were started immediately, this backlog of research might be enough to overcome the technical problems and a suitable product put on the market. Until such an effort is made, however, synthesized proteins remain very much in the future.

Currently, there is considerable excitement among food technologists and chemists over the possibility of growing microorganisms, such as bacteria and yeast, on the black liquor derived from paper pulp manufacture, from cane and beet sugar molasses and from crude oil and coal as a method of vitamin and protein synthesis. The French have taken the lead in this research. Alfred Champagnat, Director of Société des Recherches du Groupe S.F.B.P. in France, claims that the equivalent of all the animal protein used in the world today could be produced from only 3 per cent of the world's annual petroleum production. But he also warns that while fermentation processes using microorganisms on petroleum fractions as a substrate are now possible on a small scale, the gearing up of this process to commercial production levels at low cost would "present formidable difficulties." [8] George Parman of the Food and Nutrition Board frankly says, "It will be at least ten years before we will see any possibility of human food derived via yeast on petroleum." [9]

Then there remains the problem of how the stuff tastes. Howard W. Mattson, writing in late 1965, said: "None of these exotic sources of protein from microorganisms is past the pilot stage and most are in the R and D stage. Few of the proponents have made more than a cursory attempt to test market acceptance; usually, this consists of carrying a bottle of the product to the technical meeting at which the paper is presented. I've tasted protein from petroleum, fishmeal, algae and I suppose I could get used to eating them if I had to (on a trip to the moon, perhaps?). But I'm not likely to buy them in preference to some admittedly less nutritious food to which I am accustomed just because they may have a slightly better protein balance. (Incidentally, the protein produced by all these microorganisms is still inadequate in terms of conventional animal protein)." [10]

## Incaparina

Incaparina is the only well-known "food substitute" on the market today in the undeveloped nations. It was developed by the Nutrition Institute of Central America and Panama (INCAP) located in Guatemala City. INCAP took the basic food grain of Central America, corn, and mixed it with high-protein cottonseed meal, vitamin A and tortulla yeast for Vitamin B.

I was living in Guatemala in 1957 when newspaper headlines announced this wonderful new food which was going to solve the child-feeding problems of the world. In the succeeding years it has been touted in meeting after meeting of nutritionists as one of the great achievements in our generation. Also it has received considerable publicity in the world press and in leading magazines. In fact, INCAP has had on its staff an "economic consultant" as a public relations man to push acceptance of Incaparina by the housewives of Central America. Sophisticated companies, such as Quaker Oats and H. de Sola é Hijos in San Salvador, have made special efforts to sell the product, acting both for philanthropic reasons and in hope of commercial profit.

Nevertheless, a decade later, the impact of Incaparina on Central America remains insignificant. The trouble lies mostly in the texture and bland taste. In Colombia, Quaker Oats conducted a major campaign to sell its brand of Incaparina, but with discouraging results. It has now asked AID for $150,000 a year for three years so that it can boost its sale to a profitable level. "We've distributed samples at health centers, and made heavy use of radio and sound truck advertisements," says A. J. Dimino, Quaker Oats' vice-president in charge of the project. ". . . at the lowest economic and educational levels we're trying to reach, it's very difficult to change food habits even enough to accept a free sample." [11]

"Introducing a new product in underdeveloped countries is 'a baptism of blood,'" said an executive of Corn Products International in reference to that company's efforts, so far unsuccessful, to introduce in Brazil "Enriched Maizena" to which proteins, vitamins and minerals had been added.[12]

The food tastes of a people are truly puzzling and as difficult to alter as their views on family planning.

## The Panacea of Hydroponics

"We estimate that we can grow 40 tons of algae per acre on every acre given over to algal culture equipment. This would be the equivalent of 20 tons of scarce, valuable protein and three tons of equally scarce fat per acre." [13] That was written in 1954. The title of the article was "Now — Bread from the Sea." It reflects the great excitement then prevalent concerning the possibility of producing algae as a food.

Has anyone been eating algal bread lately?

The hydroponic production of any food, be it algae or tomatoes, is an expensive and delicate operation. It can be done. No question about it. And it is done in spots where cost is of no concern — to feed the Air Force on Ascension Island in the Atlantic, in Japan immediately after the war when our troops were exposed to amoebic dysentery or at a rich manganese mine isolated 150 miles north of the mouth of the Amazon. It is expensive since 100 per cent of all the nutrients must be fed the plants (when one farms the soil, the soil does make its own contribution!) and the nutrients must be balanced precisely so as not to kill the plant — and then there are all the additional problems of keeping contaminant algae, bacteria and fungi out of the water and maintaining the elaborate pumps and equipment needed for the whole operation.

Technically, there is nothing wrong with hydroponic farming. Economically, there is. It is too expensive a method with which to feed the hungry nations. It definitely will remain too expensive for the next several decades.

## The Panacea of Desalinization

I visited Port Etienne on the completely barren shore line of the Sahara Desert in Mauretania the year before its independence. The harbor there is surely one of the unique corners of the world. Our boat with nine-foot draft inched up the long, narrow bay flanked by arms of solid sand without the slightest bit of scrub as cover. Shoals were everywhere and the navigation charts were useless, especially after we noted that one channel buoy had been moved to mark the wreck of a German ship dating from World War I. A hundred Canary Island fishing boats were anchored here and there. A wind of near gale force blew straight out of four thousand miles of Sahara Desert; the local people claim it blows non-stop year round except for one enchanted evening a year. Eventually, trying to get as close as possible to the wharfless town, we ran aground on the sand and had to kedge to get off. The shore line was oozy mush from thousands of stranded jellyfish.

Once ashore we found the citizens lively and outgoing, as in most pioneer communities, and proud of their most valuable possession, a small desalinization plant. There is no fresh water anywhere in this waste of sand; formerly, drinking water had to be brought six hundred miles from the Canary Islands. Now there was enough water from the plant to drink, but the cost for most everyone was too great for a bath, for instance.

The moral here is that desalinization, a true marvel of modern science, is today valid for such limited use as drinking water and, with larger plants, also for all normal household consumption. But not for irrigating agricultural land.

During the New York City water shortage, Governor Nelson Rockefeller supported a plan to construct a desalting plant that would turn out one million gallons per day — versus the 1.2 billion gallon daily requirements of New York City. Some experts call the output of such plants "political water" since "compared to the needs, desalting promises little relief." [14]

All over the world desalinization plants are under construction or are in operation. The Middle East has a dozen. Egypt, the Canary Islands, Libya, and several Caribbean islands have them also, while the Soviet Union is supposed to have at least twenty.[15] But when talking about desalinization as a means of alleviating the food crisis, remember that this water from the ocean is used for drinking water, *not* to irrigate plants. "So far, no one in the U.S. has been able to produce water for less than $1.00 per 1,000 gal. in existing small plants" and the cheapest desalted water is in Kuwait where, using virtually free fuel, it costs about 60 cents.[16]

Such prices are far in excess of what agriculture can afford to pay for water. In addition to the actual cost of desalinization there must be added the cost of getting its sweet water to the fields. Pumping and moving the water to where agriculture is possible will add greatly to the cost. Yet this is a possible remedy for some areas, and research is progressing.

Glen T. Seaborg, Chairman of the U.S. Atomic Energy Commission, speaking of the use of large nuclear reactors for the dual purpose of power production and sea water desalinization, has seen the possibility that irrigation water "may be produced at a reasonable cost in the 1980's." [17] A more pessimistic view is given by Hugh Nicol when discussing power sources other than nuclear energy. "Such notions for the future extension of irrigation might truly be called pipe dreams. Evaporation of sea water at present efficiency requires burning of about half an inch of oil per acre to produce enough water to irrigate an acre or, say, 40 tons of oil per year to feed one or two people." [18]

In the next century desalinization may indeed be a major factor in agriculture — but not in this century and certainly not in time to alleviate the famines.

## The Panacea of Food from the Oceans

No matter. We still have the sea left to harvest. "Harvest" is the favorite word in this field, indicating the hope to raise fish as a crop, including techniques for seeding, fertilizing, weeding, as with any agricultural plant.

No optimist is as optimistic as the food-from-the-oceans optimist. "For practical present purposes, [the sea is] a limitless source of animal protein highly suitable for human diet." [19] The ocean grows two billion tons of fish and shellfish per year which, if caught, could be enough animal protein to keep alive a human population ten times the size now living on this earth. In contrast, note that the present worldwide catch is a mere 50 million tons. [20]

Fortunately, the fishing industry is expanding — at about 8 per cent a year. Unfortunately, even now the research for the fishing industry is not "all out." For the foreseeable future food from the seas will never catch up with the protein needs of the expanding population.

### Whole Fish

Today the oceans that cover three-fourths of the planet's surface provide only about 1 per cent of man's food intake. This is an important 1 per cent, however, since it represents 10 per cent of our animal protein. Increases in the fishing industry will be important, even vital, in some parts of the world, but the increases will not stop the coming famines. In fact, famines themselves will not even cause a change in the repugnance or religious taboos of some peoples against seafood.

In addition to the fact that the oceans are not uniformly good fishing grounds and that research in this field is still in its infancy, the conservation of this resource is almost non-existent. Some species of fish already show danger of becoming overfished even at the present relatively low incidence of fishermen, as is already true of pilchard on our West Coast and menhaden and ground fish on the East Coast. Concerning most commercial species of whales the situation is so serious they are in grave danger of extinction due to lack of international controls.[21]

Present hunting methods are still traditional and primitive. "Progress" is typified in the hungry nations usually by attaching an outboard motor to the canoe or raft. For the more sophisticated commercial fishermen the industry is on the threshold of a number of new electronic gadgets which will sense the presence of schools of fish, speed up the movement of the nets, and even draw the fish to the nets. Production might well be doubled in the next ten years through the use of these new methods. Even such a doubling, however, would be little more than a palliative for the world's hunger. A second redoubling, many experts claim, will be a difficult feat to achieve on the basis of today's knowledge of the fishing banks and other resources of the sea.

### Fish By-products

Advocates of the fishing industry point to Peru as the classic example of how a boom can develop overnight, of how "something" can happen which we are not expecting. In the last ten years fishing in Peru has exploded from a flyspeck to 18 per cent of the world's total fish landings.[22] Equally important, this has been a crucial factor in saving the Peruvian economy. Fishmeal is now the major export of the nation.

This growth of the fishing industry in Peru is "unequalled in the history of industrial fisheries development." [23] How did it happen? Perhaps the chief reason that it happened at this particular time is that fish-processing equipment was suddenly on the market at bargain prices. This happened because the sardine industry of Califor-

nia collapsed when the fish "just disappeared" and the herring industry of Norway collapsed when the fish "just disappeared." The
Californians and the Norwegians cast about for a new area to fish
and remembered Peru; it had long been known that this coast,
unique in the world, teemed with anchovy. Simultaneously, research conducted in the temperate zones was bringing about a revolution in chicken farming; this opened a huge new market for the
fishmeal feed that now supplies protein to chickens. This juxtapo-
sition of events made the development of this fishing resource economically possible.

A sour note in the Peruvian fishing boom is that no one knows
how long it will last. It is based solely on anchovies and little is
known of their life cycle. Worse, little is being done to conserve
this resource.

Do not expect that fishmeal, as an additive in man's food, will
have an impact within the next ten years. For, "under the best
conditions, there will be a long lead time during which the plants
producing fishmeal will operate at less than capacity. There will be
the additional hurdle of the very word 'fish' on the label which
isn't going to make the job any easier in most countries, since it
will raise at least the suspicion of new methods in cookery. All told,
it will be an uphill job, worth doing but tough." [24]

## *The Panacea of Agricultural Research*

Dr. J. George Harrar, before assuming the presidency of the
Rockefeller Foundation, headed for many years an imaginative and
successful agricultural research program in Mexico. Few men know
as well as he the difficulty in getting conventional agriculture to
thrive in a hungry nation; also, few men are so well acquainted
with the level of current agricultural research throughout the
world. In 1966 he testified before the House Committee on Agriculture, saying:

It would be unrealistic to believe that the current [world food short-
age] could be solved through some technological breakthrough which
could bypass conventional patterns of agricultural production or make
them unnecessary. Much has been said and written about the utilization of microorganisms, i.e., bacteria, fungi, and algae, as potential ma-

jor sources of protein; a breakthrough in the photosynthetic process has
long been prophesied; greater and more efficient utilization of marine,
brackish and fresh waters for food production is often stressed; the
conversion of certain petro-chemicals to protein substances is a clear
possibility; and there are many other ingenious ways to add substantially to world food supplies once the economic and technological obstacles have been overcome. All of these are potentially valuable. They
merit investigation, experimentation, and, where economically feasible,
application. Added together they cannot, however, be expected to reduce significantly demands on conventional agricultural practice in any
foreseeable future.[25]

   This brings us back to the impasse of trying to feed the new
millions of mouths from today's land with today's seeds and
today's agricultural techniques, and preferably feeding them with
foods they already know. To increase production within this
framework means, essentially, growing two ears of corn where only
one now grows. This can be done only with new seeds, new techniques. This means research.
   What are the chances for such an agricultural revolution by
1975?
   It is often said that American agriculture has experienced a revolution since World War II. When one considers crop production
figures, this is certainly true. The genesis of the revolution, however, began long before World War II, specifically with the Morrill
Land Grant College Act of 1862 and the Hatch Act of 1887 which
furnished the base for the first organized research in agriculture. It
has been a cumulative, snowballing process ever since. Prior to
World War II more than one-third of all federal money spent on
research was allocated to agriculture. This was (until 1938) consistently more than was spent, for instance, on the research and
development of the army and navy. (In contrast, agriculture today
receives only 1 per cent of the federal research budget, with defense, NASA and Atomic Energy receiving the bulk of the
funds.)[26]
   Part of the background of success in agricultural expansion has
been, of course, our great geographical asset of level land well
suited to mechanization, the deep, virgin soils and good climates.
Without the research, however, these lands would never have ap-

proached today's production. In varying degrees, the same story applies to the few other food surplus countries. An added factor is that since they are also within the temperate zones it has been possible to benefit from each other's research.

In the tropics, the home of the hungry nations, so far there has been almost no research. Two exceptions are the sensational increases in corn production in Thailand and wheat production in Mexico. Optimists hopefully say that if this can happen in these two countries, why not elsewhere? They overlook the long, painstaking research that went into these two isolated successes.

The Thailand success did not happen overnight. My close friend and one of the world's most dedicated scientists, Dr. I. E. Melhus, began research on corn in Guatemala in 1942 (Guatemala is the original home of the corn plant). Invited in 1950 to advise the agricultural program in Indonesia, he took along samples of several of the Guatemalan corns he had improved. Apparently, this was the first time corns had been transferred dirctly from the American tropics to the Asian tropics (in contrast to all the previous ones transferred from temperate zone United States and Europe) and they performed amazingly well. The fame of these corn lines spread among the few American agriculturists in the area and some found their way to Thailand. With further testing and selection, a corn variety was finally released which did, in fact, produce an agricultural revolution of sorts in Thailand. The crop in eight years increased from almost non-existent production to a 1963 export of $104 million, the fourth largest corn export in the world.[27] But this did not "just happen." Counting the work in Guatemala, the "miracle" took twenty-one years in the making.

The recent Mexican wheat success is similar. The Rockefeller Foundation had concentrated on a wheat research program in Mexico, headed by Dr. Norman Borlaug, since 1944. The reason that a similar success in wheat is not told about Peru or Colombia or Upper Volta or Iran is that they did not have Borlaug or his equivalent. The impact of this research on Mexican wheat production is shown in the table on page 74.[28]

Before this research program began, Mexico imported half of the wheat consumed and wheat imports were the largest dollar drain on the economy. "Virtually all government officials and farmers

WHEAT PRODUCTION IN MEXICO

| Year | Cultivated Area (in hectares) | Yield (kg/hectare) | Production (metric tons) |
|------|------------------------------|--------------------|--------------------------|
| 1945 | 500,000 | 750 | 330,000 |
| 1950 | 625,000 | 900 | 600,000 |
| 1955 | 790,000 | 1,100 | 850,000 |
| 1960 | 840,000 | 1,417 | 1,200,000 |
| 1964 | 846,000 | 2,600 | 2,200,000 |

openly stated that Mexico did not have the climate and soil for effective wheat production and that it would always be a wheat-importing nation." By 1956 Mexico was self-sufficient in wheat and in 1964 it exported a half million tons. "The yields in Sonora and Sinaloa are currently similar to those in Denmark and Belgium, the two countries generally recognized as world leaders in yield per unit area." [29]

Officials in the other countries, including our own aid advisers helping them, forget this background of *decades* of vital research when they draw up their plans for agricultural expansion. We are not alone in this shortsightedness. An editorial in the well-respected British magazine *Nature* draws attention to the British government's neglect of overseas research and "of the crass folly of the Trend Committee in recommending the dissolution of the Overseas Research Council. Where such blindness persists it is idle to expect Britain to seize the opportunities of leadership in development that are hers even within the Commonwealth." [30]

The same article points out the pertinent factor that the hungry nations are adversely situated even to recognize the need for science in their technical development. "Practically all the science in the world today is possessed by between 15 and 30 out of the 120 countries, and these with less than one-third of the population spend more than 95 per cent of the research and development funds. From them comes almost the entire output of the world's research papers, technical reports, patents and prototypes of the new products and processes as well as the bulk of the new generation of trained research workers in science and technology." [31]

In 1964 I was active in organizing a task force formed by the

National Academy of Sciences in Washington to study the capabilities of tropical South America's agricultural research and teaching institutions. The group consisted of fifteen highly competent agriculturists. We traveled throughout tropical South America by car, boat, plane, even dugout canoe. Our individual mileage totaled more than 400,000 miles. The final conclusion of the group was that current research efforts in the area are totally inadequate to cope with our primitive knowledge of how to use the tropics and, worse, virtually no such research is planned for the future. In other words, the existing capabilities for agricultural research, even if money were supplied from American sources, could not carry out the projects necessary for solving the economic problems hamstringing today's tropics.

A significant reason for this is that within the local governments and also within the planning committees of the aid-giving governments, agriculture and the agriculturist have been consistently downgraded to minor position.

In 1962 I made a study of the educational backgrounds of the Ministers of Agriculture in Latin America. There were then in that position (of those whose educational backgrounds could be determined) six army officers, four lawyers, two doctors and one who held an undergraduate degree in animal husbandry. Is it any wonder that agriculture is poorly supported at the cabinet meetings in those countries? In contrast, each Minister of Health was himself a medical doctor. Because a man is a trained agriculturist does not mean he will make a good Minister of Agriculture, nor does an M.D. necessarily make a good Minister of Health. Nevertheless, in the cabinet meetings it is easier to visualize an M.D. arguing more persuasively for the health share of the limited national budget than an army colonel arguing for the agricultural share. Today the "make-up" of these cabinets is essentially the same as in 1962.

In the entire history of Latin America I know of no president in any of the twenty republics who was educated in agriculture, although the area is almost wholly agricultural.

This situation will not change in the next ten years. In 1962 of the 10,541 students in the universities in Central America (tomorrow's leaders) only 187 were studying agriculture. Worse, this slim percentage has been getting thinner and thinner during the

1960's. Nearly all Latin American countries have decreased their percentage of university students studying agriculture during the past decade. For instance, Mexico from 3 per cent to 1 per cent; Panama from 4 per cent to 2 per cent; Dominican Republic from 2 per cent to 1 per cent. Of 105,000 Latin American students enrolled in the United States during the decade 1956-1965 only 5 per cent studied agriculture.[32]

The field of agriculture is not only downgraded, it is regarded as socially inferior for a student to study it, in contrast to the "respected" professions of law, architecture, medicine.

Can United States aid money change this? During the next ten years we are committed in one way or another to provide $10 billion to Latin America.[33] Unfortunately, there is nothing to indicate that our aid officials plan to make any special effort to upgrade the prestige of, or to increase official interest in, agriculture. In April 1965 not one of the seventeen AID Mission Directors in charge of the AID programs in Latin America was a graduate in any form of agricultural study. In fact, the only one who had what might be called a "science" or technological background was an industrial engineer. Our AID program is in the hands of economists, bankers, budgeteers and out-of-office politicians. Agriculture is seldom represented and carries small weight as these officials push panaceas from their own background.

The foregoing picture for Latin America applies equally to Asia and Africa. If for no other reason, it is a false hope to expect a revolution in agriculture in the hungry world by 1975 — there is no one to lead the revolution.

One of the greatest obstacles to overall development and progress in underdeveloped and emerging countries is the scarcity of trained people. It takes a surprising period of time to identify, educate, and provide research experience for the future educators, research scientists, administrators and other specialists needed to develop a modern agricultural society. Failure to recognize the magnitude of the task and the time element involved has led to failure, or at best limited success, of many technical assistance programs.

The Mexican experience [in wheat] has shown that it takes at least 12 years to develop an outstanding, mature scientist with sufficient experience and training to assume responsibilities for program direction. The advanced training period referred to begins with college graduates. . . . It will take 18 to 25 years to develop a team of highly qualified research scientists.[34]

AID money has gone into agricultural development projects, but these have been concerned almost entirely with the *superstructure* of agriculture. These include farm-to-market roads, rural electrification, cooperatives, credit facilities, increases in industrial markets. These are useful in the long run, but they do *not* increase production per acre. They will not bring about the needed agricultural revolution. They did not, remember, cause the revolution in our own agriculture; they merely supplemented it.

The trouble with research is that it is such a long, drawn-out process. While there are exceptions, the rule of thumb with any agricultural research project is that it takes twenty years (assuming that the basic idea is proved workable) for a new technique or improved plant variety to go through the necessary laboratory development, the trial and error of field testing and then eventually its acceptance out on the farms.

Such research could be speeded by the knowledge already accumulated in the temperate zones. Yet this knowledge can be applied to the tropics only through further, prolonged research. The same hybrid corn which produces 150 bushels to the acre in Iowa will produce less than 15 in Guatemala or Uganda. Our American high-producing cattle lines dry up, sicken and die when introduced into most parts of Africa and Asia. Applied research must be on-the-spot research.

It is true that a *massive* research attack on the problem could bring some striking results in less than twenty years. But I do not find such a massive attack remotely contemplated in the thinking of those officials capable of initiating it. Dr. Harrar is correct when he says: "The fact is that if through some series of miracles all that is now *known* in the field of agricultural technology could, along with appropriate materials, be applied universally and economically to agrarian societies, world food production could be expected to double or treble quite promptly. Unhappily, there is no hope of any early and major progress towards this utopia." [35]

To round out this summary of research on food crops, and in order not to sound too dismal, I point to a couple of items on the

horizon that are hopeful. If these do materialize as now anticipated, a major upsurge in the amount of food will result — but not
in time to avert the famines rushing at us.

"Just around the corner" are the much talked about new hybrid
wheats which are expected to increase yields by 30 per cent in the
United States. U.S. Department of Agriculture's wheat geneticist,
Dr. Virgil A. Johnson, says that such wheats "should be a big help
in averting the threatening global food shortage — if scientists can
overcome some genetic problems." These wheats are already "technically feasible" but, he says, they are not yet "economically feasible." [36] One cannot expect hybrid wheats to be widely used until
the 1970's and they probably will have only a token impact outside
North America by 1975.

There are also new tropical legumes reported in scientific publications. Some experts claim these will revolutionize animal feeding
in the tropics. They were first developed by the Division of Tropical Pastures at Brisbane, Australia, but unfortunately have not
been tested anywhere else. For instance, no one knows, as yet, how
they will perform in Latin America, even in those parts whose climate is similar to the Brisbane area.[37]

A recent achievement of major importance is the discovery of a
mutant gene in corn, called Opaque-2, by Purdue University scientists. This gene doubles the protein value of ordinary corn. The
great hope is that similar genes may be found in other cereals, such
as wheat and rice. If so, this could, in fact, be the greatest single
discovery now on the horizon for the feeding of the human race.
Yet it will have no effect before the famines come, partly because
of the time-lag necessary to grow the required amount of seed —
assuming that today's experiments do verify present hopes.

Overnight miracles, to underscore the thesis of this chapter, do
not happen in agriculture.

All evidence shows there is no possibility that sufficient new
technology will be developed through research in time to avert
widespread famine.

Some day the research will happen.

In medical circles they do not say, "*if* we get a cure for cancer,"
they say, "*when* we get a cure." But this is no help to the man
dying now from cancer.

## The Panacea of Fertilizers

Here is the great white hope of this year's optimists. Compared to the other difficulties of teaching modern agriculture to isolated, illiterate farmers, the problem of persuading them to use fertilizer is rather simple. Most soils in the hungry nations are poor in nitrogen. When you put nitrogen fertilizer on such land the results are easily seen. Even the untrained observer can immediately note the difference in growth, color of the plant and size of the crop. Also, fertilizer is something the farmer can handle and smell; he knows he is doing something when he puts it on.

Now, suddenly, fertilizer is the fashion. It is a short-term, mechanical process that fits in with the traditional development philosophy of crisis, impact projects. Build fertilizer plants everywhere. Ship more and more fertilizer everywhere.

The need for fertilizer is indeed great. The hungry nations have 55 per cent of the world's arable land and 70 per cent of the population, but they used only 10 per cent of the world's output of fertilizer in 1962.[38] Note, moreover, that much of the fertilizer they use they apply to non-food crops. In Latin America, for instance, most fertilizers are used on export crops such as cotton, sugar, coffee and bananas, not on basic food crops for domestic consumption. Actually, the consumption of fertilizer in the developing countries is increasing at an annual rate of 10 per cent. What effect will this have on increasing agricultural production? Studies on this subject have not been made and literally no one knows.

The trouble with fertilizer as a panacea is that no farmer will use it unless he knows he can make money from it. This generally requires that fertilizer trials be conducted on the spot — in the valley itself — in order to develop information applicable to the farmer's own conditions. Nor is it enough to rush something called fertilizer out to a province. It must be composed, to a reasonably accurate degree, of the specific amount of each element needed by that particular crop on that particular soil in that particular climate, i.e., to make certain the fertilizer will be economically profitable. What would be the situation if cost were of no concern, if, for instance, fertilizers were shipped free of charge to the hungry nations instead of shipping in subsidized food? The basic problem would still exist: how to use the fertilizer efficiently. Also, the farmer must know how to apply it. Putting on too much can destroy a crop, whereas using none at all will at least allow the crop to grow in its old unproductive way.

The United Nations FAO states it has carried out 9,500 fertilizer field trials in fourteen countries. The trials were intended to demonstrate the economical application of chemical fertilizer without other change in farming methods. The overall average yield increase is reported to be 74 per cent, with every field trial producing "crop values substantially greater than twice the cost of the fertilizer." [39]

I am skeptical of these figures. I have seen too many of these fertilizer trials around the world and I have seen too little clamoring by the farmer for the fertilizers. Farmers know when they are making money or losing money. As Dr. Forrest Hill, former vice-president of the Ford Foundation, says, "I've seen farmers who can't read and farmers who can't write, but I've never seen a farmer who can't figure." [40] If the fertilizer would result in significant profits, as FAO claims these 9,500 tests demonstrate, farmers would be agitating for it.

Recently, I examined some fertilizer trials on grasslands in the state of Amapá, north of the mouth of the Amazon. The resulting growth was striking and I was impressed. I asked the young agronomist there, "Where did you get your fertilizer?"

"Some of it was shipped in directly from Europe, but we received our lime from São Paulo." That is over 2500 miles away! How will it ever be possible to raise a crop that can pay for such transportation costs?

One more hardship for the undeveloped world is that phosphate- and potassium-bearing strata as well as limestone are scarce in the tropics. A fertilizer plant can manufacture nitrogen from the air, but the other mineral components must be dug from the ground and, if not found locally, often must be shipped in from extraordinary distances. Transportation cost is important because fertilizers usually are applied in the form of salts and large quantities are required per acre.

When fertilizer prices are too high and the crops they produce sell for too little, "no extension program can be devised that will induce farmers to use more fertilizer. Farmers will not and, of course, should not apply additional fertilizer under these circumstances." [41] The distinguished agricultural economist, Theodore Schultz, says:

In Japan, where farmers apply a hundred times as much fertilizer per acre as do farmers in India, the price of fertilizer is vastly lower in relation to the price of farm products. It takes less than half as many pounds of wheat in Japan to buy a pound of nitrogenous fertilizer as it does in India. In the case of rice, the difference in prices is even larger. Rice farmers in India pay between three and four times as much for this fertilizer as do farmers in Japan in terms of the price that they receive for rice, while the farmers in Thailand pay more than five times as much. Little wonder then that farmers in India and Thailand find fertilizer unprofitable. [42]

Japan, with its small area, uses more fertilizer than all of Latin America or all of Africa. It uses more than either China or India, although its cultivated area is only 5 per cent of China's and 4 per cent of India's. [43] If India were to use fertilizer at the rate that Japan does, its "requirements would far exceed the present total world output of fertilizers." [44]

Fertilizer is a mighty complex subject. There is no question it increases production, and I urge expansion of fertilizer production with all speed in every hungry nation. Eventually, fertilizer may well prove the savior of the agriculture in these countries, but not tomorrow morning, no matter what optimisms you read in the local press, such as this report in the *Kansas City Star*: "Using modern fertilizer alone, for instance, Indian rice farmers can double or triple yields. By adding to the fertilizer such other techniques as sophisticated irrigation, double or triple cropping, insecticides and improved seeds, yields can be fantastically increased." [45]

But of course! That is modern agriculture! It took seventy-five years of research for the Middle West to achieve this. At the present rate of effort in India, it will take that long there also.

### The Panacea of Irrigation

No form of agriculture is more productive than farming with irrigation water. And there is a lot of water going to waste around the undeveloped world. Thus, irrigation is often offered as a panacea for feeding the hungry regions.

The panacea, unfortunately, is governed by the law of diminishing returns. Nearly all the land that can be cheaply irrigated already is so used. Any additional land will be irrigated only at high cost. What food crops can pay this high cost? Note the cost of Egypt's new Aswan Dam where irrigation conditions are, I guess, as ideal as anywhere in the world. By the time the dam is built and the irrigation ditches are in, Egypt will have spent $1400 for each new acre irrigated (cost $1.4 billion for 1 million acres). To put this in perspective, prime Iowa land is selling now for $600 an acre.

Before pinning too many hopes on new irrigation projects, one should pause and realize that to be economically feasible specific conditions are needed: level land, a river with adequate water, a dam in the right place, canals that can be easily dug, plus a strong central authority to allocate the water and honest inspectors to police the water consumption. Such criteria drastically limit the number of acres that can be irrigated successfully.

Many people point to the recent great expansion of irrigated lands in Mexico, now one of the world's largest irrigation systems. If Mexico can do this, why cannot a dozen other countries?

The answer is research. The previously mentioned wheat breeder, Norman Borlaug, beginning his research in Mexico in 1944, had by 1953 developed some new rust-resistant wheat varieties. These opened up a profitable new business venture requiring only more irrigated land. Thus, the Mexican irrigation system rapidly expanded. Forgotten, however, is that most of the system lies north of the Tropic of Cancer in the temperate zone, and thus takes advantage of temperate zone agricultural know-how. The hungry nations with which we are most concerned are tropical.

The potential for increasing the amount of irrigated land in the world is highly debatable. FAO, for instance, is optimistic and, therefore, I draw on one of its reports. It points out the small percentage of run-off from rivers that is now being utilized in South Asia. It then estimates that, after allowing for run-off which could not be utilized for irrigation, and assuming the land were available and commandable, possibly 650 million more acres could be irrigated in India, 117 million in Burma, 17 million in Thailand, and 5 million in Ceylon.

Commenting on why this land in South Asia is not now irrigated, the report says that over the centuries "agricultural practices have adjusted themselves to the rhythm of the monsoon. . . . Thus, both farmers and the government agricultural services have accustomed themselves to a system of predominantly monocultural cropping. Such irrigation schemes as have been developed in the postwar years have been directed mainly at insuring against failure of the monsoon rather than for irrigation during the dry season." [46] Thus, if all these acres were properly irrigated, the major increase would come only if the farmer started growing two or more crops a year from his land.

There is always somebody chiding the tropical farmer because he is getting only one crop instead of two or three. The chider, probably, has never tried doing this himself.

I have. For one year only. And I was busier than that one-armed paper hanger!

On the south coast of Guatemala (a "monsoon area") I tried a crash program to increase some corn seed. The local government had loaned me a piece of land which had been confiscated from a previous opposition leader. The title to the land was thus a little vague and I was always looking over my shoulder to see if someone was about to snatch the land away. But the real problem was that my labor force was accustomed to harvesting only one crop a year. On paper, it would be easy if one had irrigation water (and I did) to harvest two crops. On paper there was plenty of time for plowing, planting and harvesting two crops. But everything had to move like clockwork to succeed. My workers did not understand this. They permitted all those things which previously could be put off to delay them the same as always. While I was away for a few days, the hitch for the plow broke. Instead of jumping on a bus and going to the capital for a new hitch, the foreman sent the distributor a telegram for a new one and then he and the workmen settled down for a drinking party. When the distributor wired back saying the part number was incorrect, the foreman was unable to answer for three days. Before, this would have been acceptable practice.

When the second crop was finally planted, the insect problems were incredibly severe. Normally, their numbers are reduced during the long dry season, but now they were in their prime. The result was that the insects ate half the corn before it was twelve inches high. In the end, it did not really matter. Because we had put in the second crop late (due only in part to the delay with the broken hitch) the rains had already come by the time it was ready for harvesting. What little corn was in the field rotted before it could be brought in.

Raising two or three crops a year on the same piece of land is done in many parts of the tropics because of the combination of several favorable factors of which the human element is the least pertinent. In those other places where a similar combination of factors could profitably introduce the two-crop system time must be allowed for the farmer to learn *gradually* how to do it. In the process the boys (like myself) are separated from the men.

When talking about water and extending the area of irrigated land, remember that increases in population not only strain transportation, schools, food supplies, etc., but also endanger adequate water supplies for normal consumption, as we are well aware of now in the United States. Thus, at the time when an area is most in need of expanding its irrigated land the water itself may become scarce. President Johnson, when introducing a bill as a senator to accelerate water conservation, stated that by 1975 the population of the United States will be 245,000,000 and we will be consuming 90 per cent of the available water supply.[47]

In the United States during the past half-dozen years a thousand communities have had to restrict use of water. At least sixty undeveloped nations already face water shortage problems.[48]

## The Panacea of Unused Land

This is the most common of the panaceas proposed, whether by experienced officials or by traveling journalists. The jungle, the

mountain valleys, the desert fringes, the broad valleys of the Amazon, the Mekong, the Niger, all are said to be hospitably awaiting
new settlers and ready to burst into fertile production as soon as
colonization projects are set up.

A United Nations publication states there are 12.5 acres of land
available for every man, woman and child in the world today, but
that only 1.1 acres are cultivated. The publication adds that at least
2.65 additional acres are "potentially usable." [49] Equally typical is
the statement that only 30 per cent of the world's land "with food
producing possibilities" is now being utilized.[50] Brazil is said to be
able to increase its agricultural land by 150 per cent over what it
was using in 1957.[51] Similar statistics are available for Tanganyika,
Sudan, Colombia, etc. How can such figures be true? If Brazil has
so much land awaiting the plow, why do the farmers of its starving
Northeast continue to lead such wretched lives on their hopeless
soils?

If all this land really exists ready to be put into production, obviously an easy solution to the world food problem is at hand. And it
is a solution that has served the world well in the past. Since
World War II four-fifths of the agricultural increases in the undeveloped nations have come from expanding into unused land.[52]
Population pressure has pushed people farther up the mountain-
sides, farther into the wastelands. Some of this new land has become valuable when irrigated or drained. In most cases, however,
the new land has turned out to be third-rate. Only population pressures brought it into use. And, of course, we do not yet know if it
can support permanent agriculture.

The question "How much land can be brought under cultivation?"
is not a relevant question. The question becomes relevant only when we
ask "At what cost?" Someone must pick up the tab. The answer to the
latter question may help explain why Brazil, the classic example of a
country with "vast, unused land resources," is well on the way to becoming one of the leading recipients of food under our Food for Peace
program.[53]

Any land, even a mountaintop, can be brought into cultivation if
enough money and labor are put into it. Jungle land can be just as
difficult as a mountaintop. The soils are deficient in nutrients with

the jungle growth existing on its own self-made compost. Strip away this jungle growth, as has so often been tried around the equator, and without extreme cost and care a crop cannot be grown longer than a couple of years. Yet always man, in his desperation, returns to try again to conquer the jungle and usually fails. He will continue to fail until there is carried out an intensive research program on tropical agriculture in cleared jungle areas. Such research has barely begun.

Until research finds the way, failure is the fate of most farmers entering the jungle with today's seeds and today's tools.

The valley of Iata was once called "an equatorial wonderland in the heart of the Amazon Basin." The soils, as elsewhere in the Basin, are lateric. Here the Brazilian government set up an agricultural colony.

Earth moving machinery wrenched a clearing from the forest and crops were planted. From the beginning there were ominous signs of the presence of laterite, blocks of ironstone stood out on the surface in some places; in others nodules of the laterite lay just below a thin layer of soil. What had appeared to be a rich soil, with a promising cover of humus, disintegrated after the first or second planting. Under the equatorial sun, the iron-rich soil began to bake into brick. In less than five years, the cleared fields became virtually pavements of rock. Today Iata is a drab, despairing colony that testifies eloquently to the formidable problems of laterite presence throughout the tropics. . . . A generation ago an American geologist, T. H. Holland, remarked that "laterization might be added to the long list of tropical diseases from which not even the rocks are safe." [54]

Large areas of the tropics have poor, leached-out soils which automatically eliminate them from commercial agriculture as effectively as inadequate rainfall eliminates the Sahara Desert. . . . Although unforeseen new techniques of food production may be developed, those who would plan for the future of the world had best be conservative as to the prospects for expansion. In the main, expansion of the world's agriculture beyond the area now being used is a hazardous undertaking. The requirements of nature for food production are so rigid that thus far man has been able to use only a small portion of the earth's land surface and has been defeated in most of his attempts to expand his boundaries.[55]

But now even this low-grade land is used up. That which is left is truly difficult, almost impossible, to cultivate. For if this land could be cultivated on a sustained basis with today's tools and seeds, farmers would already be cultivating it.

Land that is not in cultivation lies untenanted because people can make a better living, even at starvation levels, somewhere else. On this globe of ours only 7 per cent of the total land mass combines the right texture, nutrients, temperature, topography and rainfall to permit normal agriculture.[56]

The marginal areas throughout the world that have recently been put to cultivation may be arid because of unreliable rains or may be poorly drained or may have some other basic fault. An unusually rainy period may drown out the crops. Or at the slightest absence of rainfall the cry will go forth, "Drought!" "Drought!" "Famine!" "Famine!" The famine will be genuine but the drought is not a one-time factor; it is a frequently recurring, normally recurring, feature of the climate. The farmers on this new land are farming beyond the limits, based on today's knowledge of safe agriculture.

## The Panacea of Land Reform

Agitation for land reform is heard throughout the world. The advocates claim that once the farmer is working his own land, his production will shoot up. This in itself, some enthusiasts say, can make the difference between a well-fed and a hungry nation.

If they are right, the world should have plenty of food in the next few years because land reform is on the agenda of a majority of the undeveloped countries. Most everyone, except the landowners, is for it — the legitimate farm workers, the local malcontents, the city liberals, the politicians in and out of office, and, for a surety, most foreign advisers, of whom the capital of each of these nations has its full quota.

Land reform is urged for most everywhere. It is even urged for countries where, in my opinion, the ownership pattern already properly fits the limits which local geography has placed on the land (such as in Honduras). It is urged for countries where supposedly they *finished* with land reform a generation ago (Mexico).

In August 1963 I was visiting a small farm cooperative sponsored by the United States government near Recife, Brazil. Because of the great economic and political unrest in the area, the United States aid program was helping the *campesinos* buy some land in order to show our desire to help them to become landowners. The unrest was certainly real. While I was there, four hundred men moved in on the farm next to the one I was visiting, chopped the administrator into small pieces, tossed them to the side of the road and took over the land.[57]

My strongest impression, however, was the physical appearance of this land over which the people were fighting and murdering. It was rough country with steep, grassy hillsides. Theoretically, it could be farmed, but to do so one would have to tie himself and the plow, almost, to the hillside. The soil was poor and the rainfall a gamble. Yet the officials, including our AID personnel, claimed that the low production was due to the pattern of absentee landlords who did not take an interest in the land. Possibly. More pertinent was the fact that it was just an awful piece of real estate.

My concern in this book is what is going to be happening throughout the world ten years from now. During this coming decade nearly all land reform programs of whatever type now contemplated will, if they are carried out, *decrease* agricultural production, not increase it.

Look, for instance, at Castro's Cuba. Castro is a fanatic on farming, carrying agricultural textbooks about with him and quizzing his ministers and foreign visitors on fertilizer application, pasture management, etc. Yet, even with machete-swinging Fidel in the cane fields propagandizing the cultural and economic satisfactions of farm life, even with his government pushing to increase food yields, farm production in 1963 had fallen off 20 per cent since he took the plantations away from their owners.[58] In 1966 Cuba's per capita food output was a third lower than the 1957-1959 level. A recent United States Department of Agriculture report shows that rice, root crops, corn and beans in 1965 had fallen to about half the pre-Castro level and that "the livestock picture in Cuba is almost as bleak as the food crop situation." [59]

When one thinks about it, there is no mystery as to why this is so and it does not concern whether the take-over of the land is done communist-style or democratic-style. When the landowner is thrown out, the accumulated knowledge of how to work the land is also thrown out, that is, which fields should be planted, which fields need to be fertilized, which fertilizers work and which do not, what grows best and how it is best raised. Such information will be acquired by the new owner, but this takes time.

Clear records of how disastrous such disruption of land ownership can be on the short-range basis are, of course, difficult to find because usually propaganda glosses over the facts of the years of transition. Algeria, however, makes a classic case in point.

The 22,000 French-owned farms totaling 6.75 million acres of the nation's best land were mostly nationalized in 1963. The 22,000 farms were regrouped in 2,284 "socialist production units." Reports state that the government had to pay out $146 million during the 1963-1964 crop season for equipment, upkeep, seeds, fertilizers and wages. But the income was only $64 million.[60]

Those who look to Land Reform as a quick panacea for the world food crisis, may have a solution for the next generation — not this one!

## *The Panacea of Increasing Production by Government Regulations and Price Supports*

Here one meets head-on all sorts of biases and phobias both for and against.

"What, more government controls? The trouble with all these backward countries is that already they are drowning in socialism. Their only idea of taking action is to pass a new law; they try to do everything just by a new law, a new layer of useless bureaucrats." Or so say the adherents of capitalism, a beleaguered group that includes myself.

Nevertheless, it now appears that, at least regarding agriculture in the advanced countries, government controls have had a dramatic beneficial side effect. New research on this subject and new analyses of statistics have demonstrated that these controls have played a major role in the great progress of "Western," temperate zone agriculture of the last twenty years.

The controls bring stability to market prices and a sort of guaranteed fixed income for the farmer. This gives him enough leeway in which to risk his capital on new methods, new seeds, new crops. Before, he was always tied to the constant fear that the slightest error on his part throughout the whole complex agricultural year would bring on financial disaster; he did not dare try anything except what had worked in the past.

These controls were not the cause of our great expansion of agriculture, but they played a vital, supplementary role. So it is logical to ask when and how the hungry nations can similarly support agriculture by controls. Already those with socialist bent and those who do not know how complex any form of agriculture is are jumping to the conclusion that imposition of controls will be enough. Just write them into a new law.

Alas, it is doubtful if any of these countries has advanced far enough administratively to be able to operate controls effectively — assuming that the other factors necessary to agricultural expansion are at hand, which they seldom are.

Ten years ago I attended a meeting in the capital of El Salvador called to establish standards for grades of corn raised in Central America. The dozen men attending represented United States and United Nations agencies and also various departments in the Central American governments. Corn is the number one food crop of the area and corn shortages are always occurring. The thesis was that if grades for corn could be established, then the local governments could support the price for these grades; also, the trade in corn among the Central American countries could thus be more easily promoted.

The meeting was an education for me as I had not before realized the amazing number of factors by which the developed nations grade and market their grain. Just to give an idea: Each kind of grain is divided into two or more classes which in turn are divided into subclasses. The quality of the grain for the respective numerical grades is measured by relative freedom from moisture, damaged kernels, split or broken kernels, foreign material and mixtures of other classes, and by test weight per bushel. Also it is analyzed to determine if it is sour, musty or subjected to heating in storage, if there are weevils, etc. In Central America the corn would have to be graded, in addition, by color, whether yellow, white, red or purple. An additional subdivision would be whether it is a flint or hard corn, or a soft dent.[61]

In the United States grain inspectors are licensed by the Secretary of Agriculture; they cannot trade in grain or be employed by grain merchants. They are accepted as honest.

In Latin America the formation of such a corps of grain inspectors would be difficult, considering the *mordida* bribe which is so frequently imbedded in government transactions.

Yet the standards of each grade must be maintained as a basis for the government to acquire the corn. It cannot pay the same number of pesos per bushel for all the miscellaneous corn brought to the central warehouse, the weevilly corn, the moldy corn, the excellent corn, the so-so corn. And the true-blue honest grain inspectors would be only one part of the necessary administrative machine.

The evidence, the empirical evidence, is that it is a rare country that has the resources, human or financial, to conduct the sort of bureaucracy that a thoroughgoing price control program for agricultural products requires. Some day the others will have, but not tomorrow and not within the next decade.

Wise government regulations and price supports efficiently administered may some day assist agricultural production in the undeveloped world. Success will come, however, not with controls alone but rather in conjunction with improved technologies and other conditions. This will not occur before famine becomes a way of life in many of the hungry nations.

## The Panacea of Private Enterprise

At the meetings of the incredibly varied kinds of business groups, trade associations and the rest of capitalism's infrastructure, one often hears stirring speeches that it is up to the businessmen to go out into the needy nations and get on with what government has failed to do. Capitalism will succeed where socialism has floundered.

Capital can supply tools and machinery, pesticides, fertilizers, provide training in modern methods. Most important of all, U.S. capital can create an atmosphere that is conducive to self-help. In countless analyses of the subject, one fact stands out: that is the lack of incentive in the poverty-stricken, potentially rich farmlands of the Third World. The factors inhibiting food production are traditionalism, lethargy and hopelessness. . . . Capital generates incentive by producing goods and creating demand, and it widens the distribution of the fruits of labor. This is the market system so familiar to Americans.[62]

Or so says *Fortune*, mouthpiece of modern capitalism.

It all sounds straightforward, especially as the key fault of these "lethargic" foreigners, it is implied, is their failure to roll up their sleeves and go to work on their "potentially rich" farmlands.

As a firm advocate of American-style capitalism (which is a far, far cry from Adam Smith), I have long agreed that the most solid and quickest way to carry onward the overall economic development of the "emerging" nations is to give free rein to the capitalists, both local and foreign.

In 1964 I wrote *Hungry Nations*, which attempted to explain the several factors that hold back these countries from succeeding in their development plans. It contained a chapter on how the science and technology which are the foundation of so many of today's major industries could often be a more effective tool than government dollars. This chapter received considerable publicity and I had calls from a number of private companies in different fields asking that I discuss with them how they could give assistance to these nations.

The resulting talks reaffirmed to me that there is a great latent interest on the part of American businessmen to do something active in behalf of development abroad, both philanthropically and in the hope of at least a modest profit. These men are aware that their companies have unique talents. Since, however, their job is not that of economic development, they do not know how to adapt those talents to such activity.

One of the companies that approached me had already sent a committee of their officers to discuss this objective with FAO officials in Rome, had talked with several foundations in New York and had met with AID personnel in Washington. This is one of America's leading companies, with branch factories abroad and other wide experience in international trade. Officials everywhere welcomed the company's representatives and gladly discussed the company's interest in helping the developing nations. Nowhere, however, was any one of these non-business agencies geared to help this company find a role fitted to its capabilities.

When the company engaged me as a consultant in tropical agricultural development, the decision was made to go ahead with a new project without regard to cooperation or assistance or backstopping from either the American or foreign governments. After setting up its own advisory board of development technicians, the company launched an undertaking which, although still in the formative stage, may well become, I feel, a major factor in increasing the potential of the tropics.

I tell this story to emphasize that even a large, international company does not find the road wide and paved and stretching straight ahead when it sets forth on its quest to help the hungry world.

An AID official has told me about his agency's requesting two large American companies to develop a chemosterilant to sterilize rats and birds which destroy such a major portion of the harvests in the hungry nations. These two companies were uniquely qualified in this field and they quickly agreed to undertake this worthwhile and needed project. Nevertheless, as of this writing, a year later, the contracts have yet to be signed; in fact, they probably never will be signed because of the red tape injected by government legal officers who prevented their various agencies from breaking away from established routines to meet a new situation.

I daresay a good case could be drawn up to demonstrate that one of the major handicaps faced by an American company going into new fields abroad is the restrictions and conflicting interests imbedded within the assorted action groups of the American government, including and especially Congress.

Government, as many of those who try to do business with it will wearily testify, is a reluctant, lackadaisical partner!

The article already quoted from *Fortune*, entitled on the cover "What the U.S. Can Do about World Hunger," emphasized the value and the urgency of capital investment abroad. Yet of the two examples of imaginative thinking along new lines described in the article one was stalled by a banker saying he thought "it was a fine notion but pretty idealistic and he was not sure that [the proposer] had figured out a feasible debt-equity ratio." [63] As for the other, a member of the cabinet considered it "admirable in concept" but questioned "whether enough attention had been given to its nuts and bolts." [64]

The nuts and bolts and also a feasible debt-equity ratio may some day be resolved for most of these ideas. But the process will take too long. Even if all such proposals were concentrated in the single field of agricultural development the results will not be forthcoming in time to catch up with the race between people and food.

In these countries foreign corporations and individual entrepreneurs cannot today make meaningful investments without the firm and continuing support of the local government. Unfortunately, for a variety of psychological and political reasons such support is seldom available. And always and forever hanging like the sword of Damocles over the head of each and every private investor abroad are "the political instability, threats and rumors of expropriation, systems of pervasive discretionary regulation, prospects of rapid inflation and devaluation, and other novel features of overseas investment." [65] It takes a brave executive to venture his company's capital into such an environment when the goal of the venture is not to secure a normal business profit but to help the helpless — and when the "helpless" ones too often leap to bite the hand stretched forth to help them.

The troubles of working with government agencies, both American and foreign, are compounded by the fragmentation of the components of the business sector. Individually, they are usually too small to push aside the blocks imposed by government and to carry on this struggle for a long period — probably a period of several expensive years. The necessity for the company to make a profit, even a minor one, in an altruistic program creates a weakness that too often cannot be overcome.

Capital investment by private investors could indeed be the Deliverer of the twenty-first century when today's dominant theories of socialism have been played out and when the government agencies have learned to turn wholeheartedly and actively to private entrepreneurs for help. But capital investment as a panacea cannot save the world in the decade ahead. It is too loose-jointed, it is too amorphous, it is headless. The very strengths of diversity and decentralization and individual risk-taking that maintain success for the system in the United States prevent concentrated, all-out, quick, right-now action in extending investment projects into the hungry nations.

## The Panacea of the Unknown Panacea

It is always possible that, like the Greeks who erected the temple to the unknown god — to the god who might have been overlooked — that I, too, have overlooked some panacea in this discussion, something that is new, different, revolutionary. I have not discussed a number of things that are on the horizon, such as spun protein fibers derived from soybeans and which chew like real meat, or the pumping of oxygen into brackish water so that rice can be grown in otherwise valueless swamps, or growth regulators which increase the fruit size without affecting the size of the plant. Nor have I discussed climate control and the possibility of making rain fall when and where it is needed. Or perhaps I have failed to discuss a series of small, known things (such as farm-to-market roads, food storage and processing systems, etc.) which, if the hungry nations put them into practice, could bring about enough change to stave off the food crisis.

Unfortunately, agriculture is too complex a process to be revolutionized by any single process or technique, no matter how energetically it is pushed.

The question is sometimes asked: If the United States can send a man to the moon why can't we help India, Nigeria and Brazil to improve their agricultures? The answer is that improving the agricultures of India, Nigeria and Brazil is a more complicated problem than sending a man to the moon. The problem of sending a man to the moon can be solved by scientists and engineers using computers and the vast store of scientific knowledge now available. Improving agriculture in the developing countries is more complicated because it involves people and education and social change — particularly since it involves 2 billion people.[66]

## Conclusion

If a hungry nation were to give total time, attention and money to the single, narrow problem of increasing local food production — while at the same time striving to lower population growth — then there could be hope of an escape from the impending famines.

No nation seems ready for such Draconian action.

The tragedy is that the expansion of population carries within itself the infection that leads to further and further decay. Once a person is born he demands certain necessities in addition to food. For instance, shelter. For instance, drinking water. For instance, clothing. For instance, a degree of physical safety. These are basic. At the next higher level he demands housing, not just a roof. He demands also some sort of education. A stable community, if only to protect his children. Medical service. At higher levels come all the sky-tinted things wrapped in what today are called "rising expectations."

My point here is that each of these items (shelter, clothing, drinking water, education, medicine, and all the etceteras) compete within the economy for the time, attention and money of both the individual and of the national government. As the population increases, these demands become greater in quantity and in stridency.

The one word that sums it up best is "urbanization," although the same conflicts occur in most rural countrysides.

Colombia is an example. Its population will double within twenty years. This means that what you have to do in five to ten years is to double all the facilities that were created in the last two hundred years.[67] In the midst of this turmoil of doubling the housing, doubling the water supply, doubling the education, doubling the police, doubling the clothing, the improvements in agriculture needed to stop the famine remain stillborn.

Many of the optimists who feel that there are panaceas which will enable the hungry nations to improve quickly their agriculture in the next ten years suffer from a fallacy which dominates the thinking of too many officials and observers, namely, that these undeveloped countries are really just in about the same position as today's developed countries were fifty years or so ago.

This is not the case. Today's undeveloped nations have only a fraction of the crop land per person that the now-advanced countries had at the similar stage of development. Population growth rates of the undeveloped countries are far higher than the developed countries ever had. The excess people today have no significant opportunities for emigration. They have little opportunity to move into usable uncultivated areas.

In reviewing all the proposed panaceas for increasing food production during the next decade, the conclusion is clear: there is no possibility of improving agriculture in the hungry nations soon enough to avert famine.

Thus, the amount of food per person will continue to decline in the future as it has been doing the past few years. No panacea is at hand to increase the productivity of the land, just as no miracle will arrest the population explosion. Those who would turn their hopes to the chemist and his synthesis of food or to microorganisms growing on artificial media or to the other hopes are speaking of another century, not this one.

Today there is no practical alternative to obtaining food except by farming the land already under cultivation. Nor do we have a practical way to increase production from that land in time to avert the famines and resultant civil unrest of the 1970's.

# 4

## In Times of Stress Do People Retrogress?

Until now I have been concerned with the tangible things of too many people in the undeveloped world, too little food, and too few solutions in the test tubes and research fields. The combination of these three surely means trouble.

There is, in addition, one intangible factor to be considered, a thing as slippery as quicksilver and as unstable as nitroglycerine and just about as powerful, namely, the character of the citizens in these undeveloped countries and the quality of the leadership in charge of the government when the crisis of food shortages deepens.

In the developed nations the leaders are backstopped, generally, by citizens who are literate, physically healthy, somewhat sophisticated politically and, most important, long trained in the traditions of self-government. Self-government means solving one's own problems through one's own leaders.

In contrast, in many undeveloped nations there is no tradition of national self-government except, if at all, tribal forms of rule. Many of the nations are fresh from anti-colonial campaigns, whether with guns or only propaganda, wherein the sanctity of government was reviled and scorned. People do not recover quickly from the contamination of revolution and of agitation against the virtue of government. Thus, instead of striving patiently and with self-control to make their post-colonial government function, it is natural for them to revert to more revolution and more agitation to overthrow the new government as well. In such cases the leaders who rise to power are backed not by a sophisticated electorate but usually only by emotional groupings. Because these are mostly illiterate they are especially subject to demagogues and wild rumors.

Everyone hopes this is for them only a time of transition. Americans particularly should be able to sympathize with this sort of situation in view of our own time of troubled transition between our revolution and the constitutional convention which set up a strong central government. Afterwards, the United States maintained a high degree of stability, most probably because the restless ones and the impoverished ones were drained away to the empty frontier generation after generation.

These nations of the undeveloped world are, almost without exception, today in the midst of the process of finding themselves, of constructing for themselves a workable form of self-government. For some this transition process will end within a few more years. For others, such as certain of the Latin American nations, the process is still going on after a hundred and twenty-five years. Now these nations are soon to be faced with the major crisis of food shortages and resulting civil disturbances and, for many, famines. How will these people respond to this crisis? Can they endure the strain and maintain viable communities?

It is often said that in a time of stress the individual reverts to his true self. Probably so. But should this be said of a nation? What is the "true self" of a nation, whether of a composite one like the United States or of a homogeneous one like Norway? The question is even more confusing with relation to the new nations whose boundaries were so haphazardly drawn by the colonial powers for their own colonial purposes (including those not-so-new boundaries in Latin America).

A nation's leaders, whether the dictator decreeing everything by himself at the top or the cabinet and prime minister acting in parliamentary fashion, must usually be accepted as reflecting the "true self" of a nation. With them must also be ranged the lower officials, both those of the bureaucracy and of governors out in the provinces, all of whom are to carry out the orders sent down from the top.

When the crisis of famine threatens, how will all these react, either individually or as a group?

It is difficult to answer this because both leaders and public strive simultaneously to achieve the physical comforts of modern life and to retain the nation's old customs and beliefs. Yet there is no evidence, so far, that the modern physical life can be attained without sacrificing, to a major degree, the old customs. Even if all groups were to go eagerly full force along the road to modernization, there would still be powerful psychological drags. These drags would arise from the conflict between old beliefs and new ideas that hold back the nation from success, certainly from success within the short time left before famines begin.

It is the drag of these mental blocks that I now take up.

## The Psychological Drag of the Countryside

During the Korean War I was stationed for a while at the American Embassy when it was in Pusan. This was the period when Seoul, the capital, was practically a deserted city, reduced from a population of 750,000 to 50,000. Although the communists had been pushed back to the Panmunjom Line, Pusan remained the temporary capital, an anthill of troops, officials, refugees. Everything that can go wrong in the Orient went double there. The G.I.'s hated it. Everyone hated it, including the Koreans.

I did, too, until one Sunday I walked out beyond the farthest heap of refugee shanties and into the open countryside. In this wartime period transportation was hard to come by and I had not before been outside the city. Now, a hundred yards beyond the shanties I moved into a beautiful agricultural scene, peaceful and idyllic, lying between blue-hazed hills and the scalloped shore line of the sea. During later hikes I learned of the many ways in which the war had disrupted the life here just as harshly as in the formerly placid, provincial city of Pusan. On the surface that Sunday, however, all was serene as the farmers tended their little fields and everyone I met on the winding paths smiled and nodded to me. It was easy to understand why tourists, as they traveled in the old days between Japan and Peking, used to think Korea was one of the most delightful of countries.

In Pusan all was hustle and rushing around within the bleak,

ugly setting of a semi-modern Oriental city. In the countryside the
life continued at the same old rhythm within the framework of
ancient customs; the war would be a passing thing as had been all
previous invasions and alien occupations. The countryside would
survive and the old customs and beliefs and superstitions and
strengths and weaknesses would go on. Anthropologists and sociologists and economists would note changes between this decade and
the last one, but these would seldom be changes at the core of the
life out there in the countryside.

Today in the developed nations there is not too much contrast
between the life of the countryside and the life of the cities. The
jobs are different (as the cowhand's job is different from a subway
guard's) and the tempo is different, but everyone dresses about the
same, eats the same food, worries about politics to the same degree
and is diverted by the same entertainments. In some western European countries there remain pockets of the old-fashioned, isolated
peasants, but these are pockets, nothing more. The citizenry is generally homogeneous.

In the undeveloped nations of Asia, Africa and Latin America
this is not so. The countryside forms a sharp contrast to the cities.
The rural people live a life quite different from that of the city
folk.

There is, for instance, the moral code of the national religion
and this always seems to be stronger in the countryside; thus, the
rural people are generally sturdier in a moral sense and more able
to endure prolonged disaster than the mercurial, prone-to-panic
city folk. The one group relies on its own strength to survive; the
other group riots and runs to the government.

Also in the countryside are the hidebound rural superstitions
both of that same religion and of the old customs that so often
stand in the way of every effort the city makes to bring progress to
the nation. I mention religion as only the most obvious of probably
several psychological forces that can divide and dissipate the effort
of a group of citizens intent on "modernization."

When one argues how fine it would be if these countries would
start right away the various programs of birth control and agricultural reform and everything else that outsiders (like me) advocate

so urgently, he should not forget the dead weight of oh so many factors that will block such action within the very minds of the leaders.

It is a problem in ambivalence. Each leader, each minor official is affected. They sit at their desks in the city and they are sincerely committed to the policy of modernizing their nation. When things go well and all is peaceful and orderly around them they see clearly the benefits that this modernizing will bring. But when crises arise, such as the imminent crisis of famine, then to what extent will they maintain the "modern" mental attitude of the city? To what extent will they revert to the ancient anti-modern customs of the nation's countryside?

The trouble is that I doubt if any people can project both the rural and the urban points of view simultaneously. If they decide that they do indeed want to maintain all the old national customs, habits and strengths of the countryside, then I do not argue that they have made the wrong choice. Yet they must forgo most, if not all, of these, if they opt for the modern life of the city. Of such is the history of what is called "progress." In the present rush of urbanization in the United States we already have lost much of the old moral sturdiness of our own traditional countryside. This does not necessarily mean, however, that the future life of the cities cannot (when the problems of urbanization are conquered) become equally moral and stable even though the standards of morality will be quite different.

Too often the visiting foreigner believes a local official is "Western" just because he has adopted "Western" dress and is conversant with "Western" culture; the foreigner believes the official has accordingly put aside his native dogmas and taboos. The vital factor is the degree to which the official will maintain his new "Western" (city) habits and way of thinking at a moment of stress and will not revert into his ingrained background. Obviously, the official himself, even if he stops to think about this abstruse problem, cannot give the answer.

In *The Rains Came* by Louis Bromfield there is a character study of an Indian official who prided himself on his total acceptance of Western habits and culture, and who sneered at all the "native" things around him. Yet when catastrophe threatened he reverted completely to his own boyhood superstitions and "native" outlook.

So it is that, as the foreign businessman or official or journalist from Europe or the United States makes his rounds inside the city, whether Cairo or Khartoum, Pnom-Penh or Karachi, Lima or Managua, he is so often lulled into believing that the undeveloped nation is progressing into the modern world. The men he deals with wear Western business suits, they knowledgeably discuss international politics and market fluctuations, they are at ease at a cocktail party. More important, these men sincerely look upon themselves as modern, they are not playing a role as they talk about driving their country forward within all the varied areas of education, transportation, industrialization, social reforms, slum clearance.

Thus, the visitor, looking out the office window at the flowing traffic and hearing the typewriters in the adjoining room and the ring of telephones, accepts the man at the desk as modern. The traffic may be more bullock carts than autos, the typewriters may be backed by an incredibly overstaffed bureaucracy, the telephones may need a half-hour for a call to be through, the man at the desk may, behind the pleasant, sincere exterior, be oddly remiss at ever doing what he says he will do, but the visiting Westerner rationalizes these faults as remnants of the old order that soon will grow less and disappear.

Alas, he forgets about the countryside beyond the city. He forgets the old rural traditions and thought patterns that still prevail even in the capital. He forgets that the "modernized" man in front of him is himself only slightly removed psychologically and physically from his ancient background.

The Western impact [colonialism] on these societies [of the undeveloped nations of Asia] was fundamentally a superficial one. Western rule operated on the surface of Asian life and did not affect its ponderous subterranean foundations. It did introduce some of the techniques and instrumentalities of the industrial revolution, it did build a number of imposing island cities, it did construct a new political system based on a radically new conception of law and government, it did introduce many Western ideas, notions and concepts and it did spread a knowledge of its languages among the educated classes. But this foreign system in all its aspects did not radically transform all these masses of mankind. A partial Westernization penetrated only the upper layers of society. . . . It failed to propagate its civilization or extend its spiritual citizenship to its subject nations. It clearly did not change the instincts or the character of all these peoples, nor even of their elites. While a small majority did acquire some of the technical skills necessary for a modern technological society, they understood little of the values or the ferment on which Western society as a whole reposes. They were never really culturally contaminated by the West. They only acquired a veneer of Western life; its health and vigor escaped them. Except in a few outstanding cases, there was no genuine cultural conversion of souls. Although the West ruled Asia, it never in any way converted it. And this distressing consequence, far from being a source of regret, is in fact considered as a badge of pride by many educated Asians.[1]

Edith Hamilton in *The Roman Way* comments: "[Caesar and Augustus] were Rome's only great constructive statesmen in her latter years. No other men were able to go forward with the march of events and meet new conditions with new provisions. On the contrary, all turned unanimously for help to the days of old. Go back to the virtues of our forefathers, the patriots cried, from Cicero on to the last martyrs for liberty in Tacitus' pages. The longing voiced by the whole of Latin literature is for a return to the times when Rome was simple and pious and able to bear hardship. All that men were able to do when confronted with difficulties such as never had been known before, was to look to the past, which always seems so good, so comprehensible, and try to apply to the baffling present the solutions of a life that was outgrown. The old virtues were completely inadequate for the new day." [2]

Asia with its introverted religions, Africa with its animism, Latin America with its own form of medieval Catholicism are all cut from the same anti-modern cloth of the countryside. The countryside does indeed drag at their minds, drag at their will for action.

In all Africa above Johannesburg the most advancing nation economically is perhaps the Ivory Coast, and its fine capital, Abidjan, bustles with new skycrapers and boulevards. But: "An all-pervading belief in magic is one of the realities of life in the Ivory Coast. Whatever formal religion they may have adopted (mostly Roman Catholic or Moslem), the vast majority of Ivorians still place strong faith in fetishes. [President] Houphoet-Boigny himself regularly consults with prominent witch doctors and has a reputation as a benevolent sorcerer. He does nothing to disabuse anyone of this conception and makes frank use of it to enhance his hold on the nation. 'Africa is animist,' he maintains. 'We have no right to be ashamed of our animism. It is the basis of our lives.' " [3]

Whether Houphoet-Boigny is sincere in his faith in African animism or whether he is using it as a political tool, he is in this respect typical of so many other leaders of the undeveloped nations; he is ambivalent. He is buffeted by the familiar, tried-and-true tenets of the countryside versus the alien, uncouth, but nevertheless alluring, attractions of modernization as found in the capital city.

The population of the Ivory Coast will double in twenty years.[4] Already its diet is 11 per cent below acceptable standards set for protein consumption.[5] When the belt-tightening becomes more severe and civil disturbances break out, will the nation's leadership then continue to push wholeheartedly for "Westernization" of the economy or will it instead turn to the familiar, the known, the comfortable, which would include the taboos of animism?

Morocco is another illustration of contrast between countryside and city. When I was learning my geography in high school, it had four capitals, used more or less equally by the sultan: Rabat, Fez, Meknes and Marrakech. In addition, Tangier was the site of the foreign office for dealing with diplomats.

I was stationed in the American Consulate in Casablanca for a year during the war. I was surprised to learn that this large city with skyscrapers, boulevards and factories and also a seemingly ancient "medina" quarter of twisted streets and narrow, taciturn doorways was actually then only about thirty years old (the French built it out of a fishing village when they took over Morocco in 1912). I was also surprised to learn that the handsome, stately man who acted as the receptionist of the Consulate had, until about twenty years before, traditionally preceded the American Consul with drawn sword through the streets on official calls while lesser guards cleared, or pretended to clear, a passageway for the exalted one. North Africa yields to no area in its unique past nor to the recentness of its new twentieth-century ways of living.

Despite its late birth Casablanca is today a true city, although, of course, an alloy part European and part Moroccan. It has all the uglinesses and tensions of a city, but also it has the questing spirit and rising hopes that a city generates. In contrast, the former capitals of Marrakech and Fez are now overgrown village bazaars, exotic delights to the foreigner but also a comfortable, friendly rendezvous for the Moroccan countryman. Rabat remains an administrative center. Tangier, no longer a haven for foreigners and their money, is now only a seaside resort.

In Morocco the modern man probably feels at home only in Casablanca. Yet to most Moroccan leaders Casablanca remains an alien outpost of alien culture. Just the same, it continues as the nation's metropolis and flourishes in direct proportion to the degree of modernization that the country as a whole achieves. It is the principal link, in many ways the only link, with the outside world.

The local officials and businessmen who shuttle between "Moroccan" Rabat and "European" Casablanca with perhaps weekends in "eighteenth-century" Fez and Marrakech and side trips to the, oftentimes, pre-Islamic countryside of the Berbers, do indeed lead ambivalent lives. How thin, how very thin, is the "modern" veneer of the Moroccan official as he is forced to swing like a pendulum between the extremes of customs and doctrines found within his nation.

I say this with the greatest sympathy for his predicament and with admiration for the degree to which Morocco's leadership has succeeded in shortening, so to speak, the arc of the pendulum. Someone like myself who has lived in assorted countries of the undeveloped world can perhaps dimly begin to grasp the fantastically complex nature of the mental hurdles that confront the leadership of any one of these undeveloped nations. No wonder the officials back in Washington or London or Paris, surrounded by their uniform citizenries, go off the deep end so often with the foolish directives and policy statements and budgetary nonsense which they send to their subordinates stationed in these assorted countries.

As the food supply becomes critical and the stress builds up, the head of state and the subordinate officials of the typical hungry nation will, in my opinion, turn away from the artificially modern capital and revert to the familiar traditions and dogmas of their rural heritage. The countryside will offer moral strength during the crisis, but it will not allow the nation to utilize the tools of the twentieth century in its fight to halt the growing hunger.

And as each official, one by one, reverts, will not the nation be *less*, rather than more, able to cope with the crisis?

## The Physical Drag of the City

The city is a relatively recent phenomenon in these areas, usually introduced and built up during the last century of colonialism, like Saigon, Dakar, Accra, Nairobi (Latin America has had its capital cities for a longer period of time).

The city is uniquely a European institution and, therefore, as difficult for the people of these countries to comprehend and to adjust to as any of the other alien, new things that the modern era has brought artificially to them. Historically, in Africa and Asia (except in China) the so-called cities of old were merely administrative centers, the capital of the ruler, and the sites were easily changed with the successive dynasties, like the predecessors of Baghdad, Tehran and Tunis. In time, some capitals like Seoul and Delhi did become permanently linked with the national character.

I like best the story told of the origin of Tegucigalpa, the capital and principal city of Honduras. Comayagua had been the principal center of the Spanish colonial administration. Tegucigalpa was merely a crossroads for mule trains going to silver mines some distance away, a couple of which were owned by an early dictator of Honduras. When the solid citizens of Comayagua refused to accept his mistress socially, the dictator settled down at this crossroads, which had no worthwhile agricultural land around it or other economic advantage. And so the city grew up into what is, I hasten to add, one of the most charming capitals architecturally and socially in the hemisphere, but still without any economic reason for existence.

The defects of the modern city on every continent are, as everyone shouts, indeed many. Today the slum is accepted as the symbol of the city rather than what passes for the main boulevard. Billboards and neon nonsensicalities are more in evidence than colonnades and spires. Psychologists decry how this mass ugliness will eventually vulgarize the minds and customs of the inhabitants.

This, however, is not the main defect of the city in the undeveloped nation. The defect is the overattention given to the physical problems of the city. When city mobs race through the streets, the officials must, obviously, give full concentration to calming them and to trying to solve the causes that led them to riot in the first place. Even the threat of riots (and being thrown out of office) forces the officials to give undue time and effort to city matters. Perhaps the single greatest step to stability in many of these countries would be to move the university out of the capital to a distant town so that the rioting students would, in a manner of speaking, be put in their proper place.

During the past twenty-five years when the whole world has been concerned with economic development, when the billions of dollars have flowed and the economists and technicians have been incessantly advising every hungry nation, where has this money and advice gone? Largely to the cities. Slum clearance and housing projects, sewage and potable water systems, highways leading to and from the cities have accounted for, I estimate, over 85 per cent of this aid, and so it will be in the future. Even though the nation's food supply dwindles, the nation's leaders will not be able to deprive the urban population of anything important in order to pay for the massive aid the agricultural community must have to boost farm production.

Similarly, when famines developed in the past the available food stocks, including what was imported, too often were kept to feed the cities, leaving the rural population to shift pretty much for itself.

When the civil disorders build up from rising food prices, the leaders will have this mental block that first, beyond all else, they must keep the city people quiet. As the prime national policy this will surely be a foundation of sand on which to build programs aimed to save the nation.

## The Drag of Language and Racial Disunity

One of the most common myths around the world today is the mystical spirituality of a language. It is as prevalent in Europe as in Asia and Africa. So Ceylon, an adequately viable economic unit, is disrupted by opposing languages, the same as Belgium. And certain elements among the dissident tribes of southern Sudan, hanker for separateness the same as Canada's Quebecois, Spain's Basques and, I have heard, Britain's Manxmen. Even placid Switzerland has its Jura district, where the members of the French-speaking group riot (in sedate Swiss style) to get themselves transferred out of a German-speaking canton. Half the new states seem to be so harassed in varying degrees. It seems equally disruptive whether the minority has its own geographic area or whether it is mixed up within the majority.

The breaking off of Singapore from Malaysia is a precise example of how emotions overrule economic logic in these new nations. Both the Malay and the Chinese parties had their members who would not give an inch to the other race; both had their bigoted demagogues fanning the troubles; both had their politicians who placed their own ambitions above and beyond any call to civic virtue. And so they split apart. Malaysia lost its "New York"; "New York" lost its hinterland. They are now deep in a mad little commercial war that cuts both throats equally. The minority question, incidentally, remains unresolved, either for those of Chinese race in Malaysia or for the Malays in Singapore.

What country in the undeveloped world does not have its tidal eddies of disparate language groupings? What country could not tomorrow go sinking down in the riptide of race? Malaysia, the Congo, Nigeria, Ceylon, Iraq, the Sudan, Peru, Guyana are only a partial list of areas where the economic development of the country is threatened by racial brawling, where effective preparations for the crisis of famines will be formidable to initiate because there is lack of unity within the people. And when the crisis arrives and central authority weakens, will these racial and language groups orbit off into their own petty preoccupations, thus making it all the more difficult for the country to remain on even keel?

## The Drag of Nationalism

"For sheer and pervasive fervor, the love of nationhood has no equal among contemporary political passions." This results in "nations that are really not nations." [6] Nationalism is a catalyst that brings into focus much of this conflict between city and countryside, between the modern and the old, between a logically thought-out blueprint for the future and an emotional overflow of meaningless energy.

Nationalism, whether as a concrete program in behalf of, for example, self-sufficiency or as a will-o'-the-wisp torch for the spirit, is a most peculiar thing.

It is not exactly the same as patriotism for one's political unit nor is it defense of one's home nor the urge to extend power over the neighbors, all of which activities have been rampant from the beginning of time.

Nationalism is a sort of new phenomenon that appeared in Europe at various places and various times, starting a couple of hundred years ago. It accumulated force from within, like a windstorm, until at the end of World War I it had fixed most of the boundaries of the European society of nations. Essentially, it was a drawing together into a single unit of various hitherto divided peoples who had come to believe they had a common origin (or some similar common interest) and, therefore, it was high time they should remerge and thereby reestablish the glorious past.

Nationalism was a good thing for Europe, I guess, because it simplified the governmental structure by erasing the impossible number of former little sovereignties. There was also, sometimes, a cultural flowering coincidental with the formation of a nationalistic state, although the petals of the flower often were more apparent to the nationalists than to the world at large.

Now, suddenly, nationalism has been exported (and exported is clearly the word for it) to the undeveloped world where, usually, it is a totally new concept, an extra dose of yeast to ferment the populace.

This new force of nationalism is both centrifugal and centripetal to the new states. Nationalism, when it generates a unifying patriotism, is a useful, centrifugal force; when it dissipates a nation's energies on a centripetal, mystical yearning to recoup "past glories" or to "gather in the lost brothers" across the border, or to build imposing symbols just to show that this nation is as important as any other, then it becomes a disruptive force.

A basic trouble with nationalism is that everything must be reduced to a boundary line. Everybody and every clod of dirt already within the sacred boundary line is, for weal or woe, an integral part of the national ethos and must on no account be allowed to escape. Similarly, everything on the other side of the boundary that the nationalists feel in their bones is part of the ethos must be "liberated" and brought over to the correct side, including wherever some past conqueror of the right pedigree once trod his foot. Hence, the little fracases over boundary disputes — although these are no more amusing and no more improper than the old-time wars over some European duchy that had slipped by marriage to a second cousin of the other side of the house.

Pakistan, the most artificial of states, would never have been thought of except for Jinnah's distrust of the Hindu majority and/or except for his personal ambition to be a Number One, depending with which critic one talks. Yet, although it was dreamed up within the mind of one quite remarkable person, the flaws of a rampant nationalism remain the same as for the other new nations.

Another trouble with nationalism is that no one really understands or sympathizes with the nationalistic feelings of someone else. I, as an American, am a hundred per cent believer in our presently achieved boundaries and of our own cultural flowering within those boundaries, and would fight to the finish against Russia's reacquiring Alaska, or Canada's seizing that isolated northern tip of Minnesota. Yet I look on bewildered at the boundary arguments of Ecuador-Peru, Algeria-Morocco, Somalia-Ethiopia, and so on.

It is this sacred aspect of nationalism that is so uniquely disruptive in the new nations — and so expensive in consuming the nation's resources and diverting attention to matters that are usually quite extraneous to the central problem of creating a viable nation within whatever boundaries happened to have come out of the colonial period (a phrase that still applies to Latin America).

Unfortunately, the balance sheet seems to be that nationalism is one more mental handicap that the hungry nations must cope with as they confront their food shortages. It is one more checkrein that will curb efforts to organize a stable government and a stable society.

As the stress from the approaching hunger increases within these nations, nationalism will tend to deify stultifying traditions of the past, deify the supposed glories of the past, deify the taboos of restrictive religions, force the nation to squander resources on status symbols, generate political tensions with neighbors and tear down weakly established political and economic units into foolish little language enclaves.

Nationalism is one more serious handicap that will drag down the hungry nations and prevent them from organizing themselves for the turmoil of the coming decades.

## The Drag of Apathy

A direct result of malnutrition, it is now becoming recognized, is apathy, a continuing lack of energy which often lasts throughout a lifetime. All persons who slouch at the side of the road under the shade of a mango tree do not necessarily suffer from the effects of malnutrition, but it forms a good jumping-off point for my reasoning here.

Malnutrition is not, of course, new in the life of these regions, especially in city slums. Now, though, as the shortage of food increases in the years ahead, malnutrition must become a nationwide crisis.

When I lived in Mexico in the thirties the nutritionists, to everyone's surprise, decided the hitherto disparaged food of the peons — beans, tortillas, red peppers and pulque — was really a fine, balanced diet with all the necessary vitamins, proteins, and so forth. Similarly, many of the traditional, standardized diets of the lowest classes around the world have also been proved reasonably acceptable by the nutritionists. But, as already shown, it is the rare country today where the average person has enough of this basic diet to make it adequate.

Although long training for a wrestling match ought to make one better prepared for the bout, long existence on an inadequate diet will not make one better able to handle the emergency of famines. Mass apathy will be a drag on organizing for the crisis.

Malnutrition permanently impairs physical growth and there is now strong evidence that malnutrition and irreparable mental retardation are related. The specialists say that unless it is stemmed, the growing incidence of malnutrition will have a major effect on "what our civilization looks, thinks and acts like — in 1984." [7]

In Guatemala my wife befriended a woman, Lupita, whose husband had just vanished one day. Lupita lived with her five children in a shack made of pieces of cardboard propped outside the wall surrounding our garden. Such neighboring of poor and rich is normal throughout most of Latin America. The cardboard shack, kept spotlessly clean, was satisfactory enough for the dry season. All five children were under the age of six. The health of the three oldest was apparently satisfactory, but the two youngest were almost lifeless, seldom moved, appeared to be paralyzed or mentally deficient. My wife insisted that Lupita take these two to the charity clinic of the local hospital; however, Lupita reported the diagnosis to be "they don't know what is wrong." Thereupon we took Lupita and the two children to our own pediatrician, who glanced at them and said, "Malnutrition." He arranged to have the two children accepted at the hospital for a week, the longest period allowed. At the end of the week Lupita stalled (saying it would be a couple of days before she could pick them up) and managed to keep them there for another week. Finally, the pediatrician pointed out that the children had to be taken from the hospital in order to make room for others. In the end, my wife had to call for the children herself because Lupita, knowing full well the situation at home, refused to do so. During these two weeks the two children, whom we had thought to be mutes or otherwise physically deformed, had become, due to the regular feeding, almost normal. Their eyes were now bright, the lifelessness was gone. This was our first contact with malnutrition. Although we were able to help this one family until eventually Lupita returned to her Indian village, how does anyone, even a large charity organization, help an entire underfed population? Or how can the government, itself financially limited, help when the percentage of the hungry becomes too great?

Regarding Lupita, note that she had somehow managed to feed adequately the first three children. It was the extra two mouths that had proved impossible.

The tragedy is that the oncoming crisis of famines will have followed a series of intervening years of acute malnutrition. The result will be a citizenry seriously weakened both physically *and* mentally. Persons thus suffering cannot carry out energetically the government's orders nor even think through the meanings of the orders. This condition of lassitude will drag hard on the efforts of the leaders. Intelligent, energetic leadership is a wonderful accomplishment for a country, but it is mostly a wasted effort when the persons being led do not have the strength, either in body or mind, to follow their leaders. At which level will intelligent directives, as they are relayed down the bureaucratic scale and out from the capital city, become lost in the apathy of malnutrition?

## The Drag of Violence

Political scientists say it takes a generation for a nation to recover from a revolution, for a people to regain their respect for law and the thesis of government — which means to compromise and then to settle their national problems through a peaceful and orderly process. The difficulty of regaining stability is compounded if, instead of a single revolution that is over and done with, there is a series of insurrections, uprisings, coups d'état, riots, seditions, and all the other kinds of political hubbub.

Brawling of this sort is fated, unfortunately, for the majority of the hungry nations in the immediate couple of decades ahead. Specific causes may vary from one area to the next, but the affected nations have in common a degrading poverty, thin bellies, impatience with the unfulfilled promises from above and, in the end, hopelessness of ever bettering their lot. Many types of incidents can light the fuse in such a situation, but rising food prices is the most certain to produce the rioting.

Secretary of Defense Robert S. McNamara has pointed out that outbreaks of violence are endemic in the poor nations but not in the rich, also that the number of outbreaks in the poorer nations is inexorably increasing.

At the beginning of 1958, he states, there were 23 prolonged insurgencies going on about the world; as of February 1, 1966, there were 40. In 1958 the total number of outbreaks of violence were 34; in 1965 there were 78.[8]

On the basis of the World Bank's division of all nations into four categories, based on per capita income, of rich, middle-income, poor and very poor, the following statistics are pertinent: since 1958, 87 per cent of the very poor nations have suffered serious violence, 69 per cent of the poor nations and 48 per cent of the middle income. However, only one of the twenty-seven rich nations has suffered a major internal upheaval.[9]

"The conclusion to all of this is blunt and inescapable: given the certain connection between economic stagnation and the incidence of violence, the years that lie ahead for the nations [of the undeveloped world] are pregnant with violence." [10]

Even when a leader of outstanding ability arises in one of these countries what assurance is there he will not be toppled over by the next wave of violence? What range of time does he have within which to operate in order to achieve even a minor degree of "progress"?

In this fiery atmosphere of revolutions and plots and riots can any leadership adhere to prolonged plans for meeting the period of famines and for lessening the impact of hunger? Rather, will not the leadership find it safer (and easier) to regress to demagoguery for a revival of all the old popular taboos and for a revulsion against the "new" ideas?

## The Drag of Inadequate Leadership

In order to prepare for the crisis of famine the most valuable asset for a country will be a strong, stable, energetic government, regardless of whether it is a democracy, oligarchy or autocracy. In fact, there are so many overwhelming problems confronting these nations that it is difficult to see how they can possibly organize themselves for the fray even if blessed with superb leadership.

For no matter what ideal conditions prevail — and who can

define "ideal" in this context? — the challenge to the leadership will be frightening. The problems confronting these weak, storm-tossed, small or large, new or old hungry nations would challenge the ability of a Pericles or a Jefferson or a Churchill or whoever has been the best of government officials in a time of stress.

Memorable leaders will, I am sure, appear in some of those nations labeled as "undeveloped" and all honor should be given them. Some now in office are true peers of the best of the leaders anywhere. But a leader does not act alone. One must consider the *entire* cadre of aides and high officials who support and surround the head of state, and the governors of provinces and other local executives and the leading businessmen and intellectuals. Can they backstop effectively the Pericles or Jefferson or Churchill who may surface in today's hungry nation?

This problem concerns not only the leaders at the top but the entire fabric of society, even to athletics.

An international organization sent to Mexico the swimming coach of Princeton University to advise sports officials on improving the development of their national swim meets. He reported:

I have observed a complete disregard for time in all facets of Mexican life. Nobody seems to be on time — it is always a half hour, or more, late.

Time is the determining factor in swimming! This is how we decide who is best. We can't disregard time, even if we want to. . . .

The age group competition I observed was appallingly slow. It took four hours and twenty minutes to run forty heats, six and a half minutes per heat! And, the meet started two hours late! The officials must be responsible enough to report on time, and they must be efficient enough to keep the meet moving along rapidly and smoothly.[11]

The psychological drags against which a nation's leadership must fight are many:

(a) The ambivalence of the age-old countryside against the alien, distrusted city.
(b) The fetters of rigidly unchanging religions.
(c) The overemphasis on city problems.
(d) The squandering of resources on the deceits of nationalism.
(e) The apathy resulting from malnutrition.

It will be the rare political eagle who can take flight from this environment and lead his nation successfully over the hurdles these grim handicaps impose.

And perhaps the highest hurdle of all is the official's own attitude to his job, to his position in the government. "The Burmese ideal is to become a *min* — a government official — to be surrounded with all the pomp and circumstance of power and to be in a position to rule for personal profit and prestige over others. And for them it is the holding of the position rather than any particular achievement in it which is satisfying." [12]

As men, these officials will be influenced by the human traits developed from their environment.

As the food shortages intensify, ever stronger governments will be needed to keep the lid on the boiling ferment. Already the trend is clear, such as the growing number of military dictatorships (in 1965 two out of every three governments in tropical America were, essentially, military; since 1958 tropical Africa has had eighteen successful military interventions).

Strong governments do not necessarily mean, however, progress. Haiti, for instance, has its strongest government in many decades, but it has sunk deeper into chaos; its "philosophy" is a deliberate revival and strengthening of the most primitive of the Haitian folk customs and taboos.

One believes in democracy. One believes in the importance of nourishing its growth. One knows that true social advancement is most firmly achieved through a system of civilian leadership whereby trained and dedicated younger men successively rise to the top to replace the older men as they retire. Yet is such orderly management of the leadership cadre possible in the present-day societies of these nations?

Military leaders [in Brazil] have a point when they ask who else is fit to rule the country. Civilian political leadership is discredited and old-style politics are bankrupt. The traditional political parties, recently dissolved by Castello Branco, were personalistic alliances lacking any coherent program or organization. Their passing went unmourned. Their control was monopolized by the same political hacks who had been active since the thirties and whose threadbare views remained unchanged for decades.

The younger generations correctly feel that the old politicos have no answers to their country's contemporary problems. But the youth themselves (here, read anyone under 50) have yet to meet the challenge. Those who are active in politics are usually little different from the leaders they wish to replace. The majority are soft-living scions of the upper classes, whose denunciations of poverty and political repression are most frequently heard in discotheques and swank restaurants.

Even the most radical have little or no contact with the workers and peasants they plan some day to lead, and they have given little thought to grass-roots organization. Their political efforts consist mainly of composing eloquent manifestoes for each other to sign.[13]

It is not the problem of creating "modern" states. For that there is not enough time left, no matter how brilliant the leadership. It is the problem of organizing a government strong enough to maintain adequate law and order while preparing for the crisis. Keeping the lid on a boiling pot is quite a different task than turning the heat off under the pot. Military juntas seem to be the impending form of government for tomorrow's hungry nations. Unfortunately, although these may maintain order, they do not bring forth the sort of leadership which will, with singleness of purpose, forestall or alleviate the crisis of famine by enforcing population controls and bringing life to a stagnant agricultural system. For a military government is just what the name implies: one that stays in power through force, not through the free will of the people. Such a clique cannot maintain the support of the masses over the long period of time necessary to carry through policies like those affecting the highly personal factor of birth control and affecting the equally personal way in which the individual farms his land.

## Conclusion

I am anxious that the foregoing does not becloud the fact that I deeply sympathize with the leaders of these nations as they face the extraordinary complexities of their responsibilities, complexities far more awful than those which their opposite numbers must handle in the United States and Europe. I extend unstinted admiration to those leaders who succeed even slightly in pulling their people along the rocky road of "progress." Impatient critics (and impatient friends) of these nations forget the fantastic gulf between yesterday and today throughout the undeveloped world.

Here is east and central Africa of only sixty-six years ago, as described by a governor of Kenya:

Inland of the narrow coastal strip the people had no units of government of any size or stability; indeed, with a few exceptions such as Buganda, nothing beyond local chiefs or patriarchs. They had no wheeled transport and, apart from the camels and donkeys of the pastoral nomads, no animal transport either; they had no roads or towns; no tools except small hand hoes, axes, wooden digging sticks, and the like; no manufactures and no commerce as we understand it, and no currency, although in some places barter of produce was facilitated by the use of small shells; they had never heard of working for wages. They went stark naked or clad in the bark of trees or the skins of animals, and they had no means of writing, even by hieroglyphics, notches on a stick or knots in a piece of grass or fibre; they had no weights and measures of general use. . . . They were pagan or ancestor proprietors, in the grip of magic or witchcraft, their minds cribbed and confined by superstition.[14]

Many of these phrases applied equally to much of Latin America and Asia at that same time and some were in force only twenty or thirty years ago. When I first went to Mexico in 1932 some sections still had "no wheeled transport," "no tools except small hand hoes, axes, wooden digging sticks and the like," "no currency," "no working for wages," "no writing" and their "pagan spirit . . . was cribbed and confined by superstition." Some of the phrases still applied to Afghanistan when I was there in 1946 and to Laos in 1955.

I point this out not in criticism but in awe at the degree of success these peoples and their leaders already have achieved in forming and maintaining their nations despite all the pressures crowding in on them from the "modern" world — and despite all the misguided advice coming from that same "modern" world.

When I was at the United Nations in 1956 and 1957 I was particularly impressed by the knowledgeable, urbane staff of the Indonesian delegation. I wondered where these men and their equally sophisticated wives were when I was stationed in Batavia (Djakarta) in 1939 in the days of the Netherlands colony there, for certainly they were not in evidence then. My conclusion was that these qualities of the modern international life had been acquired only after independence. The native ability and latent sophistication were always present in the population, but only the challenge of independence and the challenge of the need for leadership had been able to bring the qualities to the surface.

In this chapter I have listed several complex, conflicting psychological drags that will hold back, and perhaps stop altogether, the progress of a nation. I want to make every allowance for leaders of ability who will rise to the top here and there. I want to extend sympathy for the huge psychological leap each citizen must himself make to enter even the fringe of the modern world. Nevertheless the resultant prospect must surely be, as the crisis of hunger and civil strife intensifies, that both the masses and the leaders will withdraw deeper and deeper into the refuge of their ancient customs and beliefs, their animism, their introverted religions. In the past, these tenets of the old countryside have enabled their civilizations to revive from catastrophes of war and pestilence and the ravaging of dynastic changes.

Perhaps this is not a false refuge. I do not doubt that, after the surplus populations have been swept away, these static civilizations will indeed be found once again to be more or less the same as they were in the last century and the century before. With a population cut back, perhaps, to the size of a few decades ago the traditional customs may very well succeed in organizing an adequate utilization of the national resources.

Yet regressing societies such as these cannot, in truth, withdraw from the modern world. They thereby become weak pawns of the major powers, just as they were pawns of the earlier colonialists. And when the major powers lose interest in them, those of their neighbors who gain even a slight political advantage from modernization will similarly browbeat them.

Clinging to the ancient customs may indeed provide a psychological refuge. But this leaves wide open the gates to the enemy — and makes inevitable that the leadership will not cope effectively with the tribulations arising from the ever shrinking supply of food.

# Nor Can the Resources and Talents of the Developed World Avert Famine from the Hungry Nations

> Whoever could make two ears of corn, or two blades of grass to grow where only one grew before, would deserve better of mankind and do more essential service to his country, than the whole race of politicians put together.
>
> JONATHAN SWIFT

# 5

## *The Granary Is Where the Food Is*

*Since the hungry nations of the undeveloped world cannot curb
their exploding populations,*
*Since the hungry nations cannot grow enough food to feed their
populations,*
*Since modern science cannot discover in time new sources of
food or new kinds of food,*
*Since, anyway, the leadership will be unable either psychologi-
cally or in ability to prepare these hungry nations in advance to
minimize the crisis,*
THEN this leaves only one remaining hope to save the threatened regions from the impending calamity of famine. This hope is
the developed world.

Yet the hope is limited, upon scrutiny, to just one segment of the
economy of the developed world, namely, its food crop agriculture.
Worse, the hope is further limited to just four crops of the devel-
oped world: wheat, corn, rice and soybeans. Gifts of money from
Italy, gifts of clothing from Sweden, gifts of medicines from Great
Britain, gifts of dried milk from Switzerland, gifts of fertilizer from
Germany will be welcome in the stricken nations, but only bulk
food, meaning grain, can stop the famines.

Even limiting the hope to the four key grain crops does not pin-
point the crux of the crisis. The developed world (the temperate
zone) does not grow enough rice to tip the balance. Corn as a
food for the undeveloped nations is important only when sent to
certain parts of Latin America and Africa but useless, relatively

speaking, in Asia where most of the people, even when on the brink of starvation, would have to learn how to cook it and learn how to eat it. Soybeans as a food is increasing in importance, but compared to the cereals it remains minor.

Only wheat is the prime, unquestioned source of hope for the hungry nations. And for the past seven years the world has been using more wheat than it has been raising. This has reduced world carry-over stocks by half.[1]

To divide the world into understandable components in relation to their food capacity, I need to use exact terms.

For my purposes "The West" is not an exact enough term for denoting those regions of the world that are the opposite of what I have been calling the hungry nations. "The West" has ceased to be definable. Sometimes the term is used for those nations with a western European heritage (but how about Israel, Yugoslavia or Haiti?). Sometimes it is used for those countries who oppose communist Russia and China (but how about France and Pakistan who, as of this writing, are tepid opponents?). Sometimes it is used for the industrialized parts of the world (but does this include non-industrialized Greece, fountainhead of "Western" civilization?). Nor are the other synonyms applicable which are sometimes used, such as "The Haves vs. The Have-nots," "The More Developed vs. The Less Developed," "The Envied Ones vs. The Jealous Ones," "The Strong vs. The Weak," "The Drivers vs. The Hitchhikers."

In this day of growing populations and stumbling countries, probably the terms "developed" and "undeveloped" are adequate, at least adequate enough to separate the lucky ones who are eating regularly from those who must beg for food or pseudo loans with which to "buy" food. A clearer term than "developed" is, I think, *self-reliant*. The self-reliant nations are those that either have excess food stocks or have their population in balance with their food supplies or have sufficient foreign exchange from industrial products or mineral resources with which to buy the food and other necessities through normal commercial channels. These are the nations unlikely to become charity cases in the future. They can take care of themselves. They are *self-reliant*.

The opposite term might be the charity nations, but that does not explain why they must receive alms. The precise term would be "insufficient." They have insufficient resources, insufficient food supplies, insufficient foreign exchange for the number of their citizens. They will be unable to take care of themselves when the troubles come. However, the most descriptive term is "hungry." They will in very truth be *hungry nations* and that is what I shall continue to call them.

Regarding the special case of Russia and its eastern European satellites one might well classify them as insufficient regarding many facets of their economies; certainly, psychologically they have the outlook of the other undeveloped nations. Nevertheless, with regard to this one factor of food, although it is not certain that in the future they will be productive enough to feed their populations, it can be expected they will be able at least to pay on the international market for whatever additional grain they need. And pay with solid foreign exchange. They will be, most likely, self-reliant.

Among the self-reliant nations there are four countries which hold a unique position. These are the ones which can produce far more wheat than they themselves consume. They are the major wheat exporters. These four are today, and will be in the future, the primary source of supply for all food-deficit nations. They are the United States, Canada, Australia and Argentina. I call them *The Granary.*

## Grain Is the Only Bulk Food

To say the obvious, if The Granary is going to feed the hungry nations, it is not going to do so by shipping tomatoes and cabbages, or even dried milk and eggs.

Many argue that food aid should rely primarily on protein-rich foods because these form the greatest nutritional lack in the hungry nations. Shipping this type of food, they claim, would be more effective and, probably, cheaper in the long run. A shipload of dried milk has from five to seven times more protein than does a similar load of wheat. Although milk is expensive to produce, soybeans are not. Today soybeans are the major source of protein derived from oil seeds and they are easily shipped. Undoubtedly, The Granary will continue to increase its soybean production and the international trade in it will expand sharply in the next few years. Soybeans already are the number three crop in dollar value in the United States (exceeded by cotton and corn). But world demand for edible oils and proteins has resulted in the American soybean crop *never* being in surplus. Thus, all sales have been strictly for dollars through private trade.[2] This situation is not likely to change radically in the future and thus soybeans cannot be regarded as a likely substitute for grain in food aid shipments.

To send grain to the hungry nations is not simply shipping carbohydrates, as so many imply. If grain were, in fact, just carbohydrates this food component could be more easily produced by raising potatoes and sugar. The advantage of grain is that it is such a well-rounded food. Wheat, rice and corn, for instance, contain 7.5 to 13 per cent protein in addition to their carbohydrates.[3] Furthermore, grain is easily stored, shipped and distributed.

Most important of all, grain is what the eaters want. Few dietary habits have to be changed. The nutritionists can rightly claim that it would be more effective to raise and ship something other than grain, but the fact that the people, even starving people, *demand* grain means that it will remain the backbone of future food aid programs.

Over 70 per cent of the farm crop land throughout the world is planted to grain. This grain provides 53 per cent of man's calories.[4] And of all the grains wheat predominates:

Wheat provides 20 per cent of all calories consumed and occupies 22 per cent of the world's crop land. Moreover, it accounts for 60 per cent of the tonnage in the world's export trade of all grains.

Rice is mostly consumed where it is grown. Therefore, the amounts available for world trade are comparable to such minor cereals as barley, millet or rye.[5] And in many areas the poorer classes are being forced to shift from rice to the lower-priced wheat; formerly, the two grains were at the same price level.[6]

Corn is a major food only in parts of Latin America and Africa. Elsewhere it is regarded as feed for livestock and chickens, and nearly all corn entering world trade is intended for that purpose.

The graph[7] on page 128 shows the trend of grain production on a per capita output basis. Note that the ability to increase grain production is in one part of the world, but the people desperately in need of it are off in quite another part.

## Canada, Australia and Argentina Do Not Give, They Sell

The key factor to remember about the international wheat trade is that Canada, Australia and Argentina sell their stocks at the international price each year, whereas the United States "gives away" 60 per cent of the wheat it exports.[8] The United States production is so huge that if it sold all its output the world price would fall below production costs. The balance which the United States does not sell at the international price (or consume domestically) it gives away as P.L. 480 Food (as discussed in Chapter 7).

The *only* major variable in the wheat trade, as presently organized, is the amount of American production left over after all commercial demands have been met.

For the decade ahead the question immediately arises as to what degree commercial demands will increase. The populations of the self-reliant nations are increasing just as steadily as those of the hungry nations, although at lower rates. Japan, formerly self-sufficient, is now a heavy importer of grain. The international consumption demands through commercial channels will continue to increase year after year. Unless Canada, Australia and Argentina can expand their production correspondingly, then the United States, other factors remaining the same, will be called upon to fill the increased commercial demand. This will decrease the P.L. 480 food left available for the hungry nations.

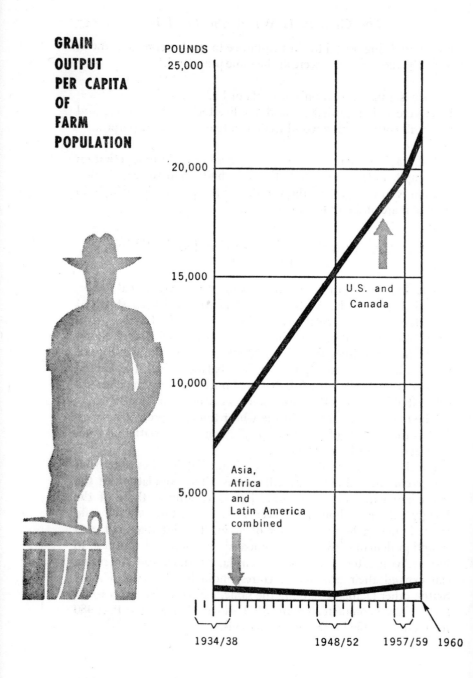

GRAIN
OUTPUT
PER CAPITA
OF
FARM
POPULATION

POUNDS

25,000

20,000

15,000

U.S. and
Canada

10,000

Asia,
Africa
and
Latin America
combined

5,000

1934/38          1948/52     1957/59  1960

Unfortunately, wheat production in The Granary, although expanding, is by no means leaping upward, as can be seen in the table.

### WHEAT PRODUCTION OF THE GRANARY, SHOWING TREND IN PRODUCTION[9]

(in millions of bushels)

| | 1955-1959 Average | 1960 | 1961 | 1962 | 1963 | 1964 |
|---|---|---|---|---|---|---|
| United States | 1,095 | 1,357 | 1,235 | 1,094 | 1,142 | 1,290 |
| Canada | 466 | 518 | 283 | 566 | 723 | 600 |
| Argentina | 266 | 150 | 190 | 190 | 300 | 340 |
| Australia | 168 | 274 | 246 | 307 | 328 | 380 |

Oddly enough, not much study has been given as to what the future production of Canada, Australia and Argentina will be. One can assume the present gradual growth trends of the past decade will be continued, but will there be an important curve upward? This is an unknown factor. Although detailed surveys of the problem are understood to be under way in these countries, the data are not now available.

Specifically regarding Argentina, its production no doubt can be greatly improved because political factors have been the principal constraint since Perón's debacle — a debacle caused in the 1940's by levying direct taxes on agriculture in order to pay for industrialization and for "self-sufficiency." From one of the most prosperous agricultures in the world it quickly degenerated to a stagnant mess and the nation has yet to recover.

There is a possibility of some increase in the amount of land that can be put into wheat production in these three nations. However, the amount of available new wheat land, such as might result from shifting acreage from other crops into wheat, is considerably less than in the United States.

The excess food producing capacity of the United States represents the only major reserve of food in the world that can readily be called forth in the race between food and people. Other major grain producing countries such as Canada, Australia and the Soviet Union do not have large areas of fertile, well-watered land that can readily be put into production. The Soviet Union may, in fact, be forced to abandon some of the marginal land brought into grain production a few years ago. Western Europe, already heavily dependent on imported foodstuffs, cannot provide food to meet the growing food shortages in the developing countries.[10]

It is doubtful that the use of any new improved technology will soon lead to major increases in Canada, Australia and Argentina. No new, improved wheat varieties are in sight for these countries. The new hybrid wheats now under intensive study in the United States, as mentioned in Chapter 3, will not begin to make an impact on our own production until the 1970's. Presumably, they will become important about the same time in Canada and, a few years later, in Australia and Argentina. As world prices go up there may be a greater use of fertilizer, increasing yields somewhat.

Therefore, in lieu of specific data to the contrary, one must assume the present wheat production trends will continue for the next ten years. The larger production in these countries will be absorbed by an overall increase of perhaps as much as 50 per cent in consumption demand from all the self-reliant countries.[11] Thus, the anticipated increases in production in these three nations will have little impact on forestalling hunger throughout the world.

The result will be that the final hope of feeding the hungry nations must fall upon America's own productive capacity.

There are three reasons why Canada, Australia and Argentina will be of little help:

(a) The above-mentioned unlikelihood of major wheat increases in them.

(b) Their internal economies are so closely tied to their agricultural exports that they cannot afford generosity on the American scale, that is, to the degree which the coming years will demand.

(c) Even if they could afford generosity at that level, these countries have not yet developed within their governments and citizenry a sense of moral duty, and this comes slowly. There is little evidence that this exists today even at a rudimentary level. During 1962-1964 Canada shipped only 100,000 tons of wheat and Australia only 50,000 tons on a noncommercial basis, an insignificant amount in comparison with the 13,500,000 tons shipped by the

United States on a noncommercial basis during the same period.[12]

The World Food Program is a clear-cut illustration that the other members of The Granary will not contribute effectively to the hungry nations either wheat or the cash with which to buy it. This Program was begun in 1963 by the United Nations' FAO as a means of collecting food, cash or services for distribution to the needy countries. The theory was that those nations without excess food stocks could donate money and those without either food or money could donate labor and services. The whole amount received would be put together with the purpose of acquiring food as an aid to economic development. The initial goal to get the program started was $100 million in donations, surely a modest sum for the entire family of nations to assemble.

Two years later $95 million had been received in pledges, but over half came from—guess who?—the United States.[13] By 1966 eight prosperous nations (Australia, Austria, Ireland, Italy, Japan, Netherlands, Norway, Sweden) had pledged a total of slightly more than $1 million.[14]

In the midst of the 1966 food crisis in India, when the United States was planning to send by mid-spring $254 million of food (plus a $250 million "loan" to buy American fertilizer), *twenty-five* other nations (including Canada) made plans to send among them a total of about $70 million in aid.[15]

Another way of phrasing this point is the following from the congressional hearings on the new Food for Peace bill:

SENATOR HERMAN EUGENE TALMADGE: Do we have any negotiations going on with Argentina or with Australia or with New Zealand or with Canada or France to try to allocate this problem [of supplying food to the undeveloped nations] fairly among the various nations who have plentiful supplies?

SECRETARY OF AGRICULTURE ORVILLE L. FREEMAN: The biggest and broadest effort to do that today is in the World Food Program of the FAO, where some 100 nations are making voluntary contributions of over $300 million for food purposes . . .

TALMADGE: How many nations?

FREEMAN: About 100 nations.

TALMADGE: What is the total amount involved?

FREEMAN: $300 million.

TALMADGE: One hundred nations, $300 million, and you are talking about a program here of $3.3 billion?

FREEMAN: The maximum.

TALMADGE: That is a rather unfair burden to place on us in view of their performance, Mr. Secretary.

SENATOR ALLEN J. ELLENDER: How much of that $300 million do we contribute, Mr. Secretary?

FREEMAN: Forty per cent of it.

ELLENDER: . . . So even of that $300 million, we contribute 40 per cent of it.[16]

The channels have long been open for Canada, Australia and Argentina to supply food or cash for the relief of the hungry nations. They have not done so. Senator Ellender also added:

We tried to get food for India. I understand we went to Australia. They said, we have no more, we sold it to China. We went to Canada. They, too, said, we have no more, we sold it to China. We went to the United Kingdom and asked for assistance in behalf of the Indians. What did they offer? To carry a few hundred thousand bushels of wheat that they will get from us. We are the only ones now that have the wheat and the grain of any amount, and my guess is that when it is all over, you will find that Uncle Sam is footing most of the bill, as we have been doing in the past.[17]

In the future it can be assumed that Canada, Australia and Argentina will continue to sell their wheat on the international market to whomever has the cash and will give only minimum token gifts to the starving. As at present, Argentina will continue to sell its wheat primarily to Europe (Argentina is the United Kingdom's "nutritional colony" [18]), and Canada and Australia will continue to sell to Russia and Communist China whatever amounts they want. In fact, Canada and Australia have a practically guaranteed market in the communist world for a generation to come.

My advice to investors looking for a good return on their money is to put it into wheat land in Canada and Australia. It's a sure thing!

## Since the United States Is the Last Hope of the Hungry Nations, What Then?

Although the United States is by far the world's largest exporter in total tonnage of wheat, it generally is only second or even third in the size of its commercial shipments, that is, what is sold for cash on the international market. To emphasize what a modest amount, relatively, its commercial shipments come to, France in 1964-1965 sold abroad just about as much wheat as the United States.[19]

The vital importance of the United States in the world food situation is not that it is a big producer of wheat (Russia's production is larger) but that it consistently produces so much more than it either consumes domestically or sells abroad. The table below gives evidence.

WHEAT EXPORTS FROM THE GRANARY NATIONS

(in millions of bushels)

| | U.S. Food-Aid Shipments[20] | Sales for Hard Currencies by the Other Granary Nations[21] | | |
|---|---|---|---|---|
| | | Canada | Australia | Argentina |
| 1965 | 547 | 434 | 237 | 155 |
| 1964 | 484 | 554 | 227 | 102 |
| 1963 | 470 | 330 | 176 | 66 |
| 1962 | 491 | 365 | 230 | 86 |
| 1961 | 456 | 342 | 183 | 70 |
| 1960 | 366 | 279 | 116 | 77 |

Even so, the line between production and the demands of consumption is indeed thin. In 1960 when its warehouses were at their fullest, the United States had only enough wheat on hand for one year of normal *domestic* consumption, disregarding entirely the needs for exports. At the same time, it had only two years of corn.[22]

No American president familiar with the climatic conditions of our country and in view of the present world situation can afford to count on average [grain] yields. . . . It is sobering to realize that no part of the world, in the event of serious crop failure, is more than one year away from critical starvation, and even the rich United States with all its surpluses is not more than two years away. Purchases on the world market may alleviate the sufferings, but no grain movements on any major scale are really feasible. There are simply no merchant navy or port facilities available for such gigantic undertakings.[23]

With the supply line from wheat producer to wheat consumer so fragile, as well as harried by weather fluctuations and politics, the establishment of a firm governmental policy to organize adequate charity shipments to the hungry nations will become increasingly chancy as food becomes scarcer. Basic to the formulation of such a policy must be the question: Will the United States have in 1975 enough wheat to keep starvation from the hungry nations?

Secretary of Agriculture Freeman says, "Yes — until 1984."

In 1966 he demonstrated his awareness of this problem by having his staff assemble essential figures both for the world food needs in the years ahead and for the capacity of the United States to meet those needs. I present on page 135 a chart [24] illustrating these figures. Note that it uses the term "grain" not just wheat. Also, it excludes Communist China from the "developing countries," a major omission.

The Secretary stated that unless the hungry nations improve their own agricultures their food *shortages* (excluding China) will grow from 18 million tons in 1965 to 25 million in 1970 and 42 million in 1975. By 1970 there will be a need for nearly twice the amount of food aid the United States is now giving.[25] By "turning loose all of our production," he said, we would only postpone the disaster for a few years.[26]

The most serious consequence of all would come at that time, probably about 1984, when the total U.S. agricultural productive capacity would no longer be sufficient to meet the food needs of the aid-recipient countries. This would lead to a breakdown of the world food economy with consequences that would range from catastrophic famine in many areas to an elemental struggle for the control of food resources. This pattern of massive food aid, by itself, would be a road to disaster.[27]

In testimony before the House Agriculture Committee, the Secretary said the deficit will reach such a size that "by 1985 there

# THE YEAR THE U.S. CAN'T FILL THE FOOD GAP

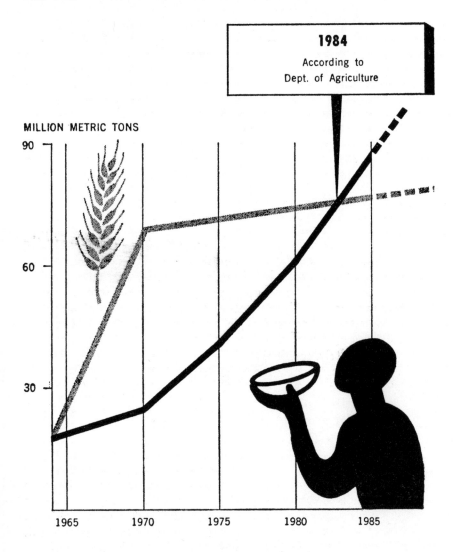

**1984**
According to
Dept. of Agriculture

MILLION METRIC TONS

90

60

30

1965    1970    1975    1980    1985

Grain that could be produced in U.S. in excess of amounts needed for domestic use and commercial exports

Food aid needs of 66 developing countries

would be no way to fill the gap." Thereupon he read to the Committee President Johnson's statement: "The time is not far off when all the combined production, on all of the acres of all the agriculturally productive nations, will not meet the food needs of the developing nations — unless present trends are changed." [28]

This testimony of the Secretary is extremely important, partly because of his official position and partly because most other world leaders have refused so far to acknowledge such a serious prospect publicly. Nevertheless, I find I must challenge his department's conclusions. The deficit gap with its catastrophes will come upon us, in my opinion, in just half the time projected by the Department of Agriculture, that is, by 1975 instead of 1984. There are several reasons for my belief:

1. *The Department's Projections of Increased Production in the Hungry Nations Are Too High.*

The projections are based on the assumption that domestic food production in these countries will increase at the rate of 2.6 per cent a year, "as under current trends." Although FAO figures show a 2.6 per cent trend for the ten-year period 1953-1963, this is achieved only by averaging out the increase for the entire decade. Unfortunately, recent years have not measured up to the vintage earlier years. In fact, the average for the last three years (1963-1966) has been 1.7 per cent.[29] For reasons already given in Chapter 3 (e.g., scarcity of usable new land) the present disappointing production figures will continue indefinitely into the future. Even the recently expanded plans to help agriculture (due to the growing awareness of the world food shortage) will not change the situation. I have traveled in too many of these countries, have seen too many agricultural ideas, schemes, paper plans and beautifully drawn-up projects disappear into thin air for me to believe that the hoped-for 2.6 per cent rate of increase is possible in the immediate years ahead. It is too big a jump over the present level of 1.7 per cent. It is wishful thinking.

2. *The Department's Projections of Food Needs in the Hungry Nations Is Too Low.*

By using the "medium" projection figures for world population growth, the Department errs on the overly hopeful side. I emphasized in Chapter 1 that population statistics have consistently been understated. Using medium figures continues to do this. It minimizes the powerful demographic forces at work today. For instance, nearly half the population in the hungry world is under the age of fifteen, the age group with the fastest rising food requirements.

Also, the Department's failure to include China in its projections gives a misleading impression of world needs. The more wheat that China buys from Canada and Australia the greater will be the dependence on the United States for filling the commercial needs of the rest of the world.

3. *The Department's Projections of American Production Are Too High.*

The Department claims that if all our crop land now in the Soil Bank (Crop Land Adjustment Program) were withdrawn, the United States could produce 70 million tons of grain for export by 1970, 72 million by 1975 and 74 million by 1980. I am sure that this is possible. Even so, optimism prevails in this implication of what the United States will and can do. For instance:

(*a*) The Department's statistics are based on the assumption that the increases will be derived from more corn grown on corn land, more wheat on wheat land, etc. Yet only certain countries in Latin America and Africa will be able to use the corn; the others need wheat. Presumably, the United States will respond by attempting to grow wheat on land better suited to corn or other crops. If this happens, the United States will not have the production capacity indicated by the Department's figures.

(*b*) It is highly doubtful that Congress will release the farmer by letting him take out of the Soil Bank all the land that has been put into it, and at no time has the Johnson administration implied an intention to do so. One reason is that the subsequent cost to the taxpayer "would be at least $2 billion higher than present programs." [30] Another reason is that too much effort went into selling the philosophy of the Soil Bank to the congressmen, the farmers and the general public to let the concept now die. Also, much of the land in the Soil Bank was put there because it was not economical to farm — and it still isn't (for instance, land in New England and Appalachia).

(c) A large proportion of the congressmen are deeply concerned over the depletion of our natural resources; the specter of the dust bowl of the 1930's still remains. Also, Congress and the public are gradually becoming aware of the peril of the steady drain of nutrients from our soils. Even intensive fertilizing is not a full substitute. This draining away of our rich resource heritage in order to give charity food abroad without financial or political return to the United States will be a major argument against "turning the farmer loose." Senator Talmadge reflects the views of many when he says that "the idea that we can use the resources of the United States, our soil and the dollars of our Treasury, which we have been spending faster than we have been collecting to feed the entire undernourished world, strikes me as being unrealistic and inconceivable." [31]

(d) Congress is no longer dominated by the farm bloc. It is in the hands of the urban dweller. The Supreme Court decision forcing redistricting by the states is the formal expression of this fact. Even before this decision the loss of farm power was foreseen. "Not so many years ago Senators and Representatives from the farming areas sought seats on the agricultural committees of the Congress, confident that the agricultural issue was a vote-getter. More recently there appears to have come a conviction that there isn't much political gold remaining in the agricultural hills. Knowledgeable legislators have been leaving the agricultural committees, evidence of judgment that the political potency of the farm issue is dwindling. The first to sense the political pay dirt was running out was that keen observer, Senator Humphrey." [32] Those who are now advocating "turning the farmer loose" are the lobby blocs who will benefit personally from this; the newly oriented Congress may recognize this and tend to discount the arguments. Land will be allowed to be withdrawn from the Soil Bank, but it is doubtful that this will be done completely.

The Department of Agriculture's forecasts must, therefore, be accepted as overly optimistic (if a food catastrophe in 1984 can be called optimistic!).

Accordingly, I superimpose on the Department's chart what I believe to be a more realistic rate of food demand and a more realistic trend in the American response to that demand. On this revised chart on page 140, my interpretation of the growing food crisis is plotted against that of the Department's on the basis of:

| *Dept. of Agriculture's Calculations*[33] | *Author's Calculations* |
|---|---|
| (1) A need to increase food consumption in the undeveloped world by 1 per cent a year so that "minimum" dietary standards are achieved by 1975. | (1) I agree as to the "need" but consider this goal to be unrealistic (for instance, in the same testimony the Secretary states this increase currently is only ⅓ of 1 per cent a year). |
| (2) Domestic food production in these countries continuing to increase at 2.6 per cent. | (2) Domestic food production in these countries continuing to increase at less than 2.0 per cent a year as indicated by today's trends. |
| (3) Population growth as projected according to the United Nations' medium estimates. | (3) Population growth as projected according to the United Nations' high estimates. |

The black lines on the chart and the first table on page 141 show the future food needs of the hungry nations.

The two shaded lines show the conflicting estimates of the amount of grain which the United States is able to produce (a figure falling somewhere between what Congress will let the farmer grow and what the land is capable of producing) in excess of what we will need for our own consumption and for our commercial exports — in other words, that which will be available for food aid to the hungry nations.

# THE YEAR THE U.S. CAN'T FILL THE FOOD GAP

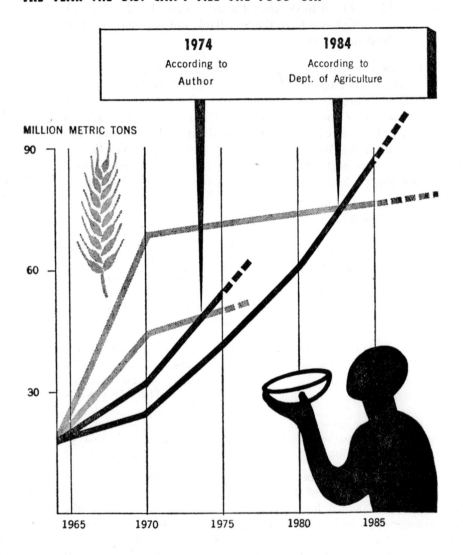

**1974**
According to
Author

**1984**
According to
Dept. of Agriculture

MILLION METRIC TONS

90

60

30

1965   1970   1975   1980   1985

▨▨▨ Grain that could be produced in the U.S. in excess of amounts
needed for domestic use and commercial use

▬▬ Food aid needs of 66 developing nations

## Future Food Needs

(in millions of tons)

| | Estimate of Dept. of Agriculture | Estimate of Author |
|---|---|---|
| 1970 | 25 | 33 |
| 1975 | 42 | 55 |
| 1980 | 62 | over 75 |
| 1985 | 88 | over 100 |

## Excess of U.S. Grain Available for Food Aid

(in millions of tons)

| | Estimate of Dept. of Agriculture | Estimate of Author |
|---|---|---|
| 1970 | 69 | 45 |
| 1975 | 70 | 51 |
| 1980 | 74 | 60 |
| 1985 | 76 | 63 |

Thus, my calculations show the United States will not be able to fill the food gap by 1975; the Department of Agriculture shows that we then can — but not after 1984. When this happens, the result, Secretary Freeman says, will be "disaster." Senator George McGovern calls it a "disaster on an enormous scale." [34]

I call the "disaster" the Time of Famines and I say that the Time of Famines will be upon us by 1975.

# The Communists' Empty Larder

No matter what the United States and the other members of The Granary decide to do (or not to do) in behalf of the hungry nations, there will be in the background, twisting and shaping the decisions, the continuing confrontation with the communist world. Although the glaring and glowering ten years from now will presumably be different from today's variety, we can assume that they will remain a factor in international affairs. Hence, the question at hand is to what extent Russia and/or China and/or the lesser communist nations will be able to interfere with, or perhaps support, The Granary's efforts to help the undeveloped world. Or will they themselves be sunk in the throes of hunger?

My own introduction to the communist world happened in Stalingrad, about nine months after the end of the great battle there of World War II. I had been transferred to the Embassy in Moscow, and the Russian plane, which was bringing me via the wartime route from Tehran and Baku, blew a tire; it was four days before another one could be brought in. The Russian passengers disappeared, never to be seen during this four-day period. I was put up in the equivalent of the only VIP room in the airport building, itself little more than a quick, makeshift sort of an affair, but the quarters were warm and the meals O.K. On the flat plain around us as far as could be seen, the wreckage of the battle had been heaped into huge mounds of twisted, rusting debris — parts of tanks, of airplanes, of everything. I was warned against the remaining minefields, but it was too bitterly cold to take any serious walks.

The plane's pilot was in and out of the airport building several times and on the second day struck up a conversation in adequate English. For the rest of the time until the new tire arrived he stayed around and we got along fine. He said he and his wife would take me to the "small" plays in Moscow and I could take them to the Bolshoi Theater "because only diplomats could get tickets." It was the sort of pleasant, easy friendship that develops between travelers. I looked forward to his showing me around Moscow.

On our arrival in Moscow the pilot shook hands warmly and said he would telephone in a day or so. When he had gone the Embassy officer who had met me said, "Nonsense. You will never see him again. He would be crazy if he tried, considering the police. The only Russians you will ever meet in Moscow are the NKVD girls and a few hand-picked jokers. You are not high enough in rank to meet any real officials. This country is sealed in tight behind a high wall and there isn't even a peephole. All these types running around as diplomats and journalists may call themselves Russian experts but they fool only their bosses back home."

The Embassy officer was both right and wrong. The pilot never did call, nor did I ever meet any Russians in Moscow except the "jokers," and this was similarly true when I was stationed for a year and a half in Communist China (in Dairen, Manchuria, 1948-1949) and never met any Chinese outside the coldly official contacts. He was also wrong, however, because there are plenty of "types calling themselves experts" who are indeed knowledgeable about the communist world. In fact, a large proportion of the best brains of our generation have concentrated on analyzing just what is going on behind the high wall. There are a multitude of peepholes and the experts can delineate the facts behind the wall without too much difficulty — although their interpretations may vary widely.

For the record, so there is no misrepresentation, I am not such an expert and the following material is set forth from the reports of others and from the considerable statistical data available.

Especially on the one subject of food versus population the statistical trends within the communist world are clear enough to form reasonable forecasts. It is only concerning the political repercussions, both domestic and international, that one must leave the statistics and enter the field of guesswork.

When one starts to predict what may be happening ten or so years from now, the future course of the Cold War is, perhaps, the most debatable factor in international politics. Maybe Russia and the United States will have become the closest of allies against a maniac China. Maybe China will have sunk again into a welter of chaos and Russia, still anti-American, moved in to pick up the pieces. Maybe western Europe will have managed somehow to slough off its persistent individualists like De Gaulle and will have succeeded in making itself a unified power and, therefore, a decisive arbiter between the United States and Russia. Maybe western Europe and the United States and Canada will have firmly forged a true Atlantic Alliance in all political and economic respects. Perhaps Canada will have emerged as second only to the United States in world power or perhaps it will have split apart. Perhaps excessive social welfare benefits will have so weakened the United States economy (look at Uruguay today) that our nation is wracked with financial and political turmoil and thus lies fearful before communist pressure. In other words, when one starts guessing the political future anything goes.

Yet this much is positive. Russia and China, like the undeveloped regions, have somersaulted from net grain exporters to grain importers. They are today food deficit areas.

Russia and China will have two choices of action. One is to pull the belt tighter and tighter and so maintain their posture of self-sufficiency, no matter to what degree malnutrition may develop within their borders. The other is to allocate more and more of their precious foreign exchange to buy food from their enemies, assuming, of course, that the enemies continue to be willing to buttress them with grain shipments.

The boundaries of the quite unmonolithic communist world are sharply defined:

(*a*) Russia and its colonies in Central Asia and along the Baltic.
(*b*) The eastern European satellites, including East Germany,

although the satellites presently seem somewhat anxious to orbit off on their own tangents.

(c) China and its colonies of Tibet and Sinkiang.

(d) The buffer state of Mongolia.

(e) The fringe states of North Korea and North Vietnam, plus the spill-over into the Pathet Lao area of Laos.

(f) Cuba.

Yugoslavia is sort of half and half, and I leave it as part of western Europe in this discussion.

## Suddenly, the Communists No Longer Export Food

Just as most undeveloped nations suddenly somersaulted after World War II from food exporters to food importers, so have the communists.

The leaders of none of these communist nations, probably, admit as yet that this somersault from exports to imports is permanent. Each has excuses of bad weather, insects, not enough fertilizer, faulty officials, inefficient, ignorant, back-sliding peasants, and so on.

Many outside observers, in tacit support of such optimism, claim that what these communized countries need is to get rid of the *kolkhozes* and state farms, restore the old incentives of peasant-owned farms and owner-controlled sale of produce. "The spreading blight of collectivized agriculture has, by the simple process of destroying human incentive, inflicted far greater losses on the world's food potential than all of the other blights combined." [1]

Although, in passing, I agree that communized, state-run farms have proved themselves by empirical demonstration to be about the most inefficient agricultural units ever devised, that is not really the point at issue here. A complete revolution in the structure of communist agricultural society, so that the peasant holdings and private trading in farm products are brought back, would certainly increase production. Yet, it is not certain that this would keep the communist world out of the food-deficit category in, for example, 1975.

## Russia's Balance Sheet

Today Russia's agricultural troubles are surely here.

From 1958 to 1964 agricultural output increased only 5 per cent. In contrast, the population during this same period increased 10 per cent.[2] The graph on page 147[3] dramatizes Russia's predicament.

And Russia's 1965 grain harvest was 12½ per cent below that of 1964![4]

In 1964 Russia paid out $367,500,000 to cover its wheat imports.[5]

It is estimated that Russia mines $200,000,000 to $250,000,000 in gold annually.[6] Note, therefore, the extra drain on the nation's exchange and gold reserves that these wheat imports cause. Russia's estimated gold reserves have, in fact, gone down one-third from the amount held in 1961, not only to pay for the grain but for all other imports, such as steel and chemical equipment for its creaking industrial plant.[7] Obviously, the more gold that must be used to buy grain the less there is available to buy industrial materials.

"Normally, the Russians sell around $200 million of gold a year in Western Europe to bridge their own balance-of-payments deficit. But just between September 1963 and April 1964 . . . their gold sales totaled $600 million. Now, with Russia's normal sales for the year still to come, and with the wheat deal on top of that, European gold dealers expect the total for 1965 to be no less substantial."[8]

And in June 1966: "The Soviet Union has again turned to Canada for wheat and flour, purchasing [over a three-year period] 336 million bushels at a cost of $800 million. The deal was described by happy Canadian officials here as the largest single wheat transaction in history."[9]

Russia's need for food imports grows ever larger. Five years ago the Soviet Union was a wheat exporter but during the last three years it has imported as much wheat as India.[10] How much longer will it have enough gold available to pay for these new imports?

# RUSSIA'S NET TRADE
# IN WHEAT AND WHEAT FLOUR

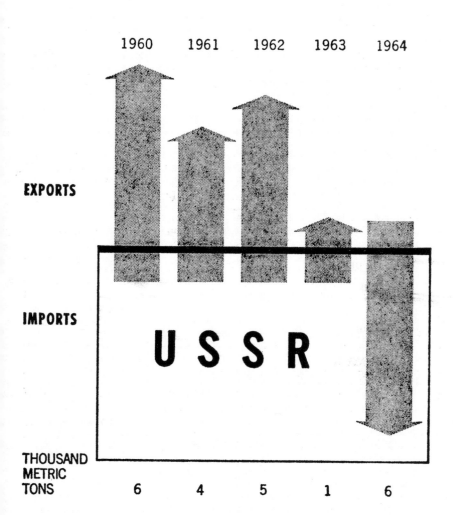

| | 1960 | 1961 | 1962 | 1963 | 1964 |
|---|---|---|---|---|---|

**EXPORTS**

**IMPORTS**

USSR

THOUSAND METRIC TONS

| 6 | 4 | 5 | 1 | 6 |

And as the need for food grows larger, will Russia be any better able than the rest of the world's hungry nations to get her agricultural house in order? I think not.

## Russia Is an Undeveloped Country

Thus, Russia is now unable to feed its citizens properly out of its own output (and meet its commitments to the satellites). Also, it is doubtful that, over the long haul, Russia will have the foreign exchange to import the full amount of food needed. This combination of economic realities is becoming the hallmark of each undeveloped nation.

There is also the parallel of cultural attitudes. In fact, perhaps the most important item to understand about Russia, other than the cold facts of its vulnerability due to food imports and the drain of its gold reserves, is its stage of cultural advancement within today's framework of developed and undeveloped countries.

In the world's eyes Russia is always ranked among the developed nations and is often regarded as just a few short steps behind the United States. Certainly, the Russians do not consider themselves on a par with the Asians and Africans. Nor do the Americans consider the Russians as "undeveloped" in view of the military threat looming out of Moscow.

Nevertheless . . . "The Soviet Union is still a poor country, with limited resources, big plans, and big problems." [11] Was there ever a more concise definition of the typical undeveloped nation?

In many parts of its economy Russia is, of course, much more advanced than any of the undeveloped nations, as evidenced by its space hardware; in other parts, however, it is on a par. It is true that success has been achieved in forging the national economy into a successful war machine. Yet this war-machine economy fails to deliver to the citizens the kind of comfortable life that the developed world takes for granted. If the people thus do not have the comforts of the developed world, one can argue that, perforce, they must be a part of the undeveloped world.

Without wandering off on this intriguing path of thought, there are other similarities with the undeveloped nations that need to be emphasized.

## Russia Has the Mental Viewpoint of the Undeveloped

The Russian government and its citizens demonstrate in an extreme degree the outlook of the undeveloped world. All the dreams and wishful thinking and all the misconceptions and faulty theories of "progress" that are rampant in Accra, Dar-es-Salaam, Rio de Janeiro, Baghdad and Delhi are dominant also in Moscow.

The Russian mental attitude toward agriculture is one of exactly the same downgrading, the same social sneering at the farmer, the same avoidance of a career in farming, that one finds throughout the entire undeveloped world from Nicaragua to Niger. Always the farmers are regarded as second-class citizens. Always the sons of farmers want to escape to the cities. Always the better students register for courses in law, medicine, engineering, the arts, anything but agriculture. Incentives for farmers are always lacking; they look forward neither to monetary profit nor physical comfort nor social acceptance. All that farmers get from their betters is propaganda to work hard and save the country.

About half the people of [Russia] live and work in villages like Selino. Some may have more agricultural machines, but they are often not used properly, or they stand idle in need of repair because there are not enough people with "mastery of technology," as Khrushchev puts it. There may be electricity in the old fashioned *izbas*, or log cabins, or it may be part of next year's plan. There is usually no plumbing, and water comes from the river, a well or an outdoor pump. There is probably one telephone, in the house or office of the farm chairman. There is generally a one-room school, but the secondary school is apt to be miles away in the nearest town. There is free medical care, but the nearest doctor or dentist may be fifty miles away.[12]

Pronouncements are constantly made from Moscow about reforming the agricultural system, about allotting more funds, about boosting farmer morale. "Give Igor More Vigor!" [13] In 1966 the Kremlin announced the most revolutionary change in the Soviet *kolkhoz* or collective farm system since the 1930's: guaranteed wages for collective farm members. But even with this reform, "most Soviet peasants will still be receiving substantially less than workers in the factories and in the mines." [14]

Historically, the farmer's earnings have had last claim to the *kolkhoz* income, coming after government requisitions and taxes, cash expenses and other costs. The "overwhelming fear of millions of Soviet rural youngsters has been that they might have to spend their lives as collective farmers, like their parents." [15]

## Russia Has the Capital City Overemphasis of the Undeveloped

Another parallel with the undeveloped world is the neurosis that the capital city is the source of all knowledge as to what is good for the nation. Thus, the bureaucrat at his desk there writes directives to solve the problems out in the steppes — and the farmers meekly assent: ". . . under Communism, politicians run the farms. Sitting in Moscow, they issue directives to farm managers 3,000 miles away, detailing what crops to plant and when to plant them." [16] "Mr. Khrushchev had a passion for agriculture. He threw himself into it, differently every day, switching crops, advisers, budgets, emphases, ministers and slogans in a way that was apparently more disconcerting inside the country than it was bewildering outside." [17]

This direction-from-the-top is also basic to the socialism which is the controlling political theory throughout nearly all the undeveloped world. Often the dividing line between communism and socialism in the administration of government is thin indeed. In Delhi, for example, the emphasis on controls and regulations and paperwork centered in the capital's bureaucracy has been, perhaps, the single greatest factor in hamstringing national progress, other than the population explosion itself. There is, in fact, a mental affinity between Moscow and Delhi in their effort to operate the nation by fiat. The Russians have been at it longer and, therefore, are relatively better at it. But the thinking is the same, and the same thinking is found in almost every other capital in the undeveloped world. One can make excuses for this in most of the countries by saying that the only educated persons are usually in the capital and many of these nations have only a few dozen citizens who can be called "educated."

Nevertheless, as in Russia, the man at his desk in the capital city is far, far removed psychologically from the troubles he is "solving" by decree.

The troubles remain unsolved.

As this manuscript goes to the publisher, reports are coming in of a bumper crop of wheat in Russia, and Russian propaganda is giving credit for this to the fine planning reforms instituted by Kosygin and Brezhnev. If the reports are true, may I point out that one, or even two, bumper crops do not change a trend. (By the way, have you ever noticed that crop failures both in Russia and everywhere else are said to be due to "unusual" drought, floods, locusts, and so on? But when a crop is good the credit goes to far-sighted planning by the officials in power.)

## *Russia's Fixation on Industrialization Is the Same as That of the Undeveloped*

Another parallel between the communist world and the undeveloped nations is the never ending emphasis on industrialization as the only Messiah. Industrialization has developed a war machine for Russia. It has not developed the *nation*. Nor will it by itself in Egypt, Iraq and Brazil. Industrialization should be only one part of the overall plan for progress, not the end-all.

The worm in the apple of giving too much attention to industrialization is that whatever progress is thus achieved is bought at the expense of agriculture (as learned by Argentina under Perón). There are many reasons for today's chronic agricultural troubles in Russia, but surely a major one must be that for two generations the overwhelming preoccupation of the Russian leadership and the Russian public has been to push industrialization. For two generations only enough attention and funds have been given to agriculture to prevent complete collapse. The most ruthless example was Stalin's selling wheat abroad during the 1920's in order to pay for industrialization while starvation was widespread in the rural areas; throughout the years, always the nation sacrificed to achieve industrialization, always agricultural development was bypassed.

## Communist Dogma Versus Communist Research

The outsider immediately asks why a massive program of agricultural research has not long since been put into operation in Russia. Part of the answer must be that it is too prolonged a project for the crash programs, the crash propaganda campaigns and the instability of personnel to allow. The Russian government, as in other undeveloped countries, is too crisis-ridden to work in terms of twenty-year programs.

There is also the extra complication of communist dogma. The press has reported on a Russian scientist who is said to have developed a new potato variety that is able to resist the frosts of northern Russia and also the virus and fungus diseases of southern Russia. However, he had utilized in his research the principle of polyploidy which follows classical Mendelian genetics — and Mendel was long disowned by the communist political theorists. For this reason the new potato variety was never given to the Russian farmer.[18] This incident was part of the well-known dominance of T. D. Lysenko in agricultural research circles for over a generation, until Brezhnev and Kosygin came to power. The long reign of Lysenko is easy to explain. "A factor which contributed to Lysenko's rise was the Soviet Union's great need to improve agriculture. In the western world Mendelian genetics was being used to develop new strains of corn and other plants and to increase agricultural productivity. But the time scale was slow, because advances depended on patient breeding of the proper genetic material and laborious crossing experiments. The Soviet government was impatient and ready to back a scientist who promised rapid improvement of Soviet agriculture." [19]

In the United States success in developing new agricultural technology has been attained via two parallel routes. One is government money and support, such as with the initial establishment of our land grant colleges and with direct allotment of funds (especially state government funds) to university and other research centers. The other parallel route is the autonomy retained by each of these research programs. Regardless of their source of funds (federal, state or private), they make most of their own decisions as to what research will be undertaken, and they remain in charge of their projects. This assures both applicability to local conditions and continuity of effort through the years — absolute essentials for effective research.

In Russia this independence of action, this freedom from bureaucratic control of the capital, is apparently impossible to achieve when all directives come from the crisis-prone official hierarchy.

Some effective research in Russian agriculture has, however, been achieved since the war, especially a few outstanding successes in pure research. But this research work has not had the support or the single-mindedness of direction that has characterized the Russian space, military and industrialization programs. In no sense has there been a massive agricultural research program to adapt the Canadian and west European temperate zone techniques. The proof of this statement is evident in Russia's dismal agricultural production record. Today's grain yield per acre is no higher than it was in the days of the Tsars.[20]

Western potato scientists have told me of visiting Russia to study potato research and production methods. "Russia is at least thirty years behind the United States in all forms and levels of potato research" was their judgment. Old potato varieties dominate production, there is no real program in seed development and what new varieties they have are badly diseased, a serious situation in a vegetatively propagated crop.

The importance of such a statement is clear when one realizes that potatoes, not grain, form the staff of life north of the Ukraine. In fact, Russia is the largest producer of potatoes and has one-third of the world's acreage.

If Russia's research on this vital crop is thirty years behind the United States, one wonders about the research programs in other agricultural areas. It is logical to assume that no surge of research endeavor, no matter how great the attack, will raise farm yields significantly by 1975.

Russia does have one major advantage not shared by most of the undeveloped world. It is located in the temperate zone. Thus, when the Moscow hierarchy gets around to allotting adequate funds to agricultural research (and to allowing enough years for fruition), the increase in production could come relatively fast.

The job can be reduced to adapting to their own harsher climate (do not forget that Moscow is a thousand miles farther north than Minneapolis) the seeds and improved techniques of fertilizer application, weed and pest control, and so on, that have already been perfected in the northern regions of Canada and western Europe.

## Conclusion on Russia

As of this writing, the current officials in control, Brezhnev and Kosygin, have initiated their solutions for getting Russian agriculture out of its doldrums. They are taking tentative steps to increase wages for the peasants and to loosen Moscow's controls over the *kolkhozes* and state farms. They have cut back Khrushchev's production target of 80,000,000 tons of fertilizer a year by 1970 to 55,000,000 tons. This 55,000,000-ton figure probably will not be achieved, but Russia should be producing in 1970 considerably more than her 1963 figure of 20,000,000 tons.[21]

If carried far enough, these new policies will, of course, increase production. By Russian standards these programs are indeed bold. Yet they will produce only limited results because they lack the underpinning of adequate scientific know-how. The officials hope to build the superstructure of a twentieth-century agriculture but have forgotten the foundation.

In the modern success story of American agriculture the chemical industries and other infrastructure components like farm-to-market roads, storage facilities and price incentives have played an important role. But the chemical industry did not produce today's hybrid corn that gives the Iowa farmer 75 bushels an acre in comparison with the 32 bushels of a few years ago. Farm-to-market roads did not produce the know-how that enables the Georgia farmer to use only 2.9 pounds of grain in place of the 5.2 pounds his father used to feed his chickens for the same weight gain. Price incentives may make it economically feasible to feed concentrates to hogs, but they did not show our farmers how to average 7 pigs weaned from a litter when 6 was considered a good average only a few years ago.

Despite the expansion plans of Brezhnev and Kosygin, the need will grow to import more food from The Granary during the years ahead. There may be occasional years when the weather is unusually good and the need to import will be reduced — but this will offer only temporary relief. By paying with gold Russia presumably will continue to receive this food — as long as the United States and its allies are willing to ship it without receiving any sort of political return, such as a lessening of Cold War tensions or such as a decrease in communist subversive operations. The time will come, however, when the United States and the other members of The Granary will not have enough grain to ship *both* to Russia and to the other nations. A choice will have to be made. Will the decision be to ship the grain to Russia without political *quid pro quo* and let the peoples elsewhere starve?

To summarize as of 1966:

In the past the Russians have done their wheat buying on an ad hoc emergency basis. The new Canadian deal (3-year contract for 9 million tons of wheat, $800 million cash on the barrelhead) is the first time that they have entered into a firm long-term contract for specified amounts. This particular bit of realistic budgeting must have been doubly galling. The deal implies that, even without climatic disasters, Russia's own crops cannot be expected to meet both the country's growing needs for food grains and fodder at home and its still considerable export commitments to its partners abroad. . . . The planned purchases from Canada are well below Russia's own "normal" export commitments to eastern Europe, Cuba and other countries, which are estimated at 5 million tons a year. . . . Given the long haul needed before Russian industry will be able to compete successfully for a much larger slice of western markets, any decision by Russia to buy considerably more grain from the West than it is now planning to buy would involve either harsh cutbacks in its industrial imports or further large drafts on its stocks of gold.[22]

Currently, one hears opinions that Russia's wheat contract with Canada is a devious method of cornering the international wheat market for the next couple of years so that no wheat will be available for China to buy. Maybe so. At least, this suggests that the amount of international wheat available is small enough so it could indeed be "cornered." Nevertheless, until such proof comes to light, the Russian contract with Canada can be accepted at face value: Russia must import wheat because it is not able to feed its population (and meet its political commitments) from the nation's own fields.

## The Eastern Europe Satellites

These seven nations (Albania, Bulgaria, Czechoslovakia, East Germany, Hungary, Poland, Rumania) have been net importers of grain during the overall period since World War II. The grain has come primarily from Russia.[23]

Now, parallel with Russia's forced buying of grain from the outside world, most of the satellite countries have had to arrange such purchases in order to feed their citizens.

The bad 1963 harvest also shifted the pattern of Soviet wheat trade with Bloc countries. In the fiscal years 1961-63 the Eastern European countries occupied 59 per cent of the Soviet wheat market. Imports by these countries from all sources totaled an average of 5.6 million tons, of which 2.9 million came from the USSR and 2.7 million from all other countries. During fiscal 1964, however, they have bought 3.5 million tons from non-Russian sources.[24]

Since their domination by Russia following the war, the history of their agriculture has been closely tied to whatever policies came out of Moscow, such as forced trading of their grain in return for Russian-manufactured goods or their manufactured items for Russian grain. At least, any deficits in grain production in the satellite countries were expected to be filled by Russia.

Although Poland did away with most of the communized farms in 1956 (now only 14 per cent of the arable land remains "socialized"), the others continue almost intact the system of state farms and collectives — 89 per cent of the agriculture in Czechoslovakia, 94 per cent in Hungary, 91 per cent in Rumania, 88 per cent in Bulgaria.[25]

Geographically, the satellites are an extension of western Europe, not of Russia. Because the climate for agriculture is a variation of that of western Europe, the adaptation of the techniques of modern agriculture already in use in Germany and France should be easy — when the leadership decides to make the effort.

Effective agricultural research, however, remains absent in each of the countries. "No Communist country has been able to raise yields of grain the last five years." [26] There is no reason for this to continue. When the leadership gives to agriculture the attention it needs (enough money plus enough years for research, plus fertilizer, equipment, travel for their scientists to learn, etc.) they can expect to increase their production much more quickly than can Mother Russia. While Russia's terrain lends itself better to agriculture, its climate and the short growing season create formidable handicaps not found in eastern Europe. Rumania, for instance, is now beginning to benefit from American hybrid corns because it is at the same latitude as our own Corn Belt. In this Rumania has been influenced by neighboring Yugoslavia which quickly became an important corn producer by simply introducing hybrid corn direct from Iowa (both regions are at 43 degree latitude).

Today these countries, taken as a whole, are marginal in the sense of importing or exporting grain. A few bad weather years and any one of them can have serious food shortages. With good weather and/or new technology the exports could become sizable. If this happens, it will be interesting to observe at which point these nations will want to cut loose from the drag of Russia. Surely, these nations will become more independent in their international politics as they realize that Russia is growing more vulnerable due to its increasing food gap. Fortunately, in population matters their annual rates of population increase are as low, or lower, than most of western Europe, certainly the lowest in all the undeveloped world.

In summary, it is within the realm of possibility that these nations may become food surplus areas within the next ten years. Whether the surpluses are shipped to Russia or to the international market will be determined by future politics. Either way it is unlikely the amount involved will have a major influence on the course which the growing world food crisis takes.

## Cuba

Cuba, no matter how you slice it, was always a peculiar place, economically speaking. Traditionally, the economy was boom or bust, with its agriculture based on the up-and-down sugar market. Production of food crops was in inverse proportion to the effort given over to King Sugar. By the 1950's, however, two items were cushioning the economy. One was American tourists whose expenditures were moving rapidly to an anticipated $100,000,000 a year. In this hemisphere only Mexico had a tourist business to match Cuba's. The other item was the American sugar quota system, one of the oddest special interest laws ever devised by Congress.

The sugar quota operates by the United States' assigning to certain selected sugar-producing countries a quota for which we will pay the import price of approximately 6.5 cents a pound, in contrast to the price now under 2.0 cents that these foreign growers would obtain on the international market. When Castro began confiscating American properties, Washington canceled (in July 1960) Cuba's quota (really just a form of subsidy) and shared it among the thirty remaining nations. In other words, even if Castro were overthrown tomorrow, it would be a devil of a job to put the eggs back together so that Cuba could again have its old quota.

With the income from American tourists and with the 4 cents gift per pound it received from the United States for the sugar, Cuba's economy was highly prosperous at the time Castro came into power. "In the days before Castro the country's standard of living was one of the highest, perhaps the highest, in Latin America, comparable to that of Italy. It was predominantly an urban and middle-class nation whose economy was steadily expanding in spite of the corruptions of the Batista regime; it was a healthy economy basically run on a private-enterprise basis. When Castro imposed communism on the nation, Cuba floundered." [27]

The basic fact of today's Cuba is that it is completely dependent on the communist world, especially Russia, to receive sufficient food to prevent serious hunger. "Raul Castro has admitted that Cubans would be starving were it not for aid from the Soviet Union." [28] Yet Russia, with her own food deficit, is indeed, for Cuba, a weak reed on which to lean.

As with the other communist countries the agricultural sector of the economy is buffeted by frantic changes in policy and bureaucratic personnel and sudden increase or sudden decrease in funds as the government strives to find a quick "solution." Every couple of years seems to bring a different policy in Cuba as to whether all effort will be given to producing more and more sugar or whether sugar will be curtailed and food crops increased. That is no way to run a farm.

Technically, there is nothing wrong in growing sugar and using the income to purchase food from abroad (or to barter it for food from the communist countries) — except, however, that because of its high cost of production Cuba loses with every pound of sugar it sells or barters. In addition, this policy leaves the nation vulnerable because one-crop economies have little room in which to negotiate when the price is low.

Not untypical was the sudden decision in early 1966 of Red China to cut in half the already agreed-to barter arrangements for Cuban sugar in return for Chinese rice. This political move against Cuba produced a crisis because rice is the customary food grain for Cubans.

"We have no resources," Castro said, "to buy this rice [which China now refused to ship] in other markets because this would be to the great detriment of other vital parts of the economy. . . . [For Cuba to try to produce the rice it needs on its own soil] we would have to revise completely our agricultural plans for the coming years, the sugar plan for 10 million tons, our fruit-production plans, and our vegetable production." He added that Cuba would have to divert land, scarce water, labor and machinery that could produce sugar worth more than 150 million pesos to produce an amount of rice that would be worth 25 million pesos. He concluded the speech by implying he did not intend to make this diversion to rice and that there would have to be belt-tightening. Rice, need it be added, is now rationed.[29]

As for agricultural research to improve the nation's food production, the situation seems to be similar to the other communist nations — a lot of official *pronunciamientos* in favor of it, but relatively little cash provided and no stability at all. Yet Castro, raised on a farm, is enamored with the subject, constantly referring to new techniques and giving a childlike faith to the future rewards of science. His attitude is similar to the superficial articles in mass publications about some new, wonderful discovery that has been made but with little attention to whether or not the discovery is really practical and none at all to the fact that it may take twenty years to put it into production out in the fields.[30]

A major handicap to Cuba's agricultural research development and extension programs is the loss of nearly all its trained agronomists, plant pathologists, entomologists and animal science specialists. At the time of Castro's take-over, I was director of the Panamerican Agricultural School (Zamorano) in Honduras. For two years I received at least one application a week from Cuban agriculturalists who wanted to work at the school. Since then I have run into these Cubans all over Latin America, working at Montecristi in the Dominican Republic, dairy farming in Puerto Rico, raising tomatoes at Belem in Brazil, tobacco on the north coast of Honduras. With so many trained men gone, who is there to give Cuba a modern technology in agriculture? The Russians? Hardly. Their agricultural experience is that of a Canadian working around Winnipeg.

Few countries in all Latin America are today so vulnerable to famine as Cuba, this once prosperous nation whose standard of living was comparable to that of Italy only a few short years ago.

## China

When, within the last hundred years and more, did China not have calamity?

Always somewhere, within its varied geography, there has been flood or drought or crop failure or locusts or bandit gangs or marching armies or, today, mercurial communists. Always there has been something. Even the classic, oft-repeated Golden Age legend that at the height of the Ch'ing Dynasty (or the Ming or the Han or whatever dynasty is mentioned) a virgin could carry a pound of gold untouched from Yunnan to Peking has the aura of the police state rather than of peace and plenty.

Now China is on the direct road to famine. The collision between population explosion and static agriculture seems truly inevitable. The only agency left to deal with this fated doom is the communist government in Peking. The resourceful farmers and the versatile entrepreneurs who might have found ways to lessen or perhaps deflect the catastrophe have long been removed from the national economy. All power rests in Peking, and the government there does appear to the outside world as a confused, unstable company.

Birth control is a pertinent example of the vagaries of communist policies. In the early 1950's, although the reality of overpopulation was already clearly recognized, the dogmatists in the party were vehement that it would be heresy to Marxist ideology to admit that the state could not take care of each and every citizen. Nevertheless, in 1956 a serious, intensive campaign in behalf of birth control became the official policy, although the announced reason was to protect the health of mothers; it was not admitted that the state could not feed all born and unborn Chinese.

Suddenly, in 1958, this campaign was canceled without even a public explanation. Presumably, the party dogmatists within the inner circles of Peking again had won out. "People were hailed as assets and it became fashionable to say there was a shortage of labor." [31]

Four years later, in 1962, a new birth control campaign was instituted and this is continuing and expanding. Yet, "the Chinese do not relate their birth-control campaign directly to the food situation. They prefer to emphasize the benefits to the health of mothers." [32]

Premier Chou En-lai stated on a visit to Africa: "We Asian and African countries are poor and backward not because our populations grow at too fast a rate, but because we have been subjected for a long period to exploitation and plunder by imperialists and colonialists." [33] Despite this official, debatable line, China was never anybody's colony (except parts of the country for a few years under Japan). Its own internal weaknesses allowed it to be pushed around by European and Japanese pressures. Never in this century nor in most of the last has it been able to govern itself efficiently. Today's firm police hand of the communists may be preferable to the earlier war lords and to the clique of Chiang Kai-shek. Yet the present government is a far cry from an efficient, stable organism.

Especially in agriculture is it demonstrated how wildly faddish the Peking hierarchy is, that is to say, how enthusiastic they are for a "solution" one year but another one later on. Although the changes are cloaked with propaganda campaigns couched in Marxist language, and although often to non-communists there thus seems to be consistency, actually it all is a series of fads, or, expressed differently, it is a running to and fro to plug whatever hole in the dike is nearest.

In 1957 there was the Hundred Flowers policy, which permitted private farm plots. Then the Great Leap Forward (1958-1961) discouraged them and emphasized industrialization at the expense of agriculture. In 1961-1962 the private plots were again allowed.[34] By 1966 the private plots had again been rooted out in some areas.[35] Now in weak trajectory is the Soaring Leap Forward which is intended to bring new vigor into the effort to get the collectivized agriculture to increase production; theoretically, it focuses the national attention on agriculture in place of industry.

"This Soaring Leap is not a carefully defined program but an amorphous set of slogans and exhortations. The Chinese have relied, since the days of Confucius, on proverbs and slogans to define virtues and goals for all facets of life. This new campaign includes strident demands that peasants grow more and better crops, that Party workers be more energetic, and that the nation prepare for the Third Five-Year Plan for economic development which begins in 1966." [36]

The propaganda campaign is real enough, and so is the emergency. Increasing production per acre, however, is not attained by planting slogans.

Famines in China will be delayed in the 1970's only as long as its capitalist enemies, namely Canada, Australia and Argentina, continue to ship grain to it. So far, China is able to pay for these shipments with cash. However, unlike Russia, it does not have mines able to produce large amounts of foreign exchange. Instead, it must somehow produce the foreign exchange out of its own economic output, and this is a tricky operation for the present Chinese economy.

One way is to sell its rice abroad and use that money to buy wheat. The rice sells at about $120 a metric ton; the wheat costs $70. The caloric values of the two foods are about the same.[37] Similarly, soybeans can be sold abroad profitably and the wheat bought at a lower price per unit.

These are, of course, agricultural products. There seems to be nothing of value that China produces industrially in large enough quantity or value to be an important factor in gaining the needed foreign exchange. It is unlikely that the export of processed foodstuffs, light manufactures, textiles, rice, sugar and opium, plus the remittances from overseas Chinese,[38] will ever provide sufficient foreign exchange to allow China to pay easily for its food imports.

Barter deals have been made with several countries whereby food is obtained, but many of these deals are politically, not economically, advantageous. Hence, the sudden partial cancellation of its rice-for-sugar barter deal with Cuba.

The Chinese purchases of wheat from abroad are using up nearly one-half of current foreign exchange earnings. The significance of these grain purchases is dramatized by the fact that during the last three years of heavy purchases the Chinese have bought only some $70 to $80 million worth of industrial plants. Moreover, the current yearly purchases of wheat, amounting to more than $400 million, exceed what the Chinese claim to have spent on importing industrial plants even during the years of the Great Leap. In short, the current constraints in the economy have called for greater actual outlays for the importation of basic necessities than Chinese propagandists dreamed of spending at the time of their greatest euphoria about the prospects for industrial development and "surpassing Great Britain." [39]

In truth, observers are surprised at China's ability so far to find the foreign exchange to pay for the food imports.

The Chinese leaders must by now regret not having started a major agricultural improvement program in the early 1950's. Such an effort, assuming that it was even debated in the higher official circles, became impossible when it was decided to produce the A-bomb. The fact that China was able to test nuclear devices in 1964 and 1965 was an outstanding accomplishment for such a poor country. It was done, however, only by concentrating the major portion of its meager scientific talents on this single goal. The other technical problems of China, including agriculture, had to be pushed to the sidelines in favor of this purely military project.

China's agricultural research problems are much more complex than Russia's. The latter's crops are grown in long belts of flat land across the Russian map, bounded, in simplified terms, by the pertinent degrees of latitude. Most of Russia suffers from insufficient rainfall and the climate is severe, but at least the problem of research is narrowed to these few belts.

In China the geography is cut up into rather small units and the climate ranges from humid tropics to the edge of the subarctic and from dry land farming to flooded rice fields. Thus, China has a formidable problem developing a research program capable of covering not only all these climates but also the sharp differences in terrain from one province to the next. Parallel with this problem is the susceptibility of the area to the natural disasters of typhoons, floods and droughts. Some day China's scientists may conquer these problems of diversity, but not in this century.

Today, the serious political observers around the world like to prognosticate about the future of China and of Asia generally. This is, certainly, a most stimulating intellectual exercise. Of the many such predictions this one caught my eye as typical of those coming out of Asia. James Reston in his column in the *New York Times* quoted Professor C. Northcote Parkinson of the University of Malaya in Singapore: "No factor in the modern world, not even automation, is as vital as the change taking place in the relationships between East and West. . . . Ours is essentially the period during which leadership has begun to pass from the West." Parkinson then predicts that by the turn of the century Asia will regain the world leadership it held from A.D. 500 to 1000 and that its present resurgence is already a scientific fact.[40]

The thought of Asia gaining world leadership by the year 2000 is intriguing. It seems so preposterous. Yet throughout history the great shifts of power, the fall of empires and the rise of others, seem to happen not so much from new strength in a people, or even great leadership, but from a weakening in the established power of their neighbors. When Genghis Khan stormed across Asia, a major factor in his success, at least until he built up momentum, was the weakness and political decay then prevalent in China and in the states of Central Asia. Ditto Napoleon. Ditto Hitler. If the United States and also The Granary fritter away their resources during the Time of Famines without firm policies on how to help the stricken countries, or if the Granary nations undermine each other with plots and fail to support each other when needed, then indeed no one knows what the international world will be like one or two generations from now.

But to believe that China, industrially weak and already on the brink of famine, can in a few decades dominate the world, or even, one is tempted to say, only south Asia, is yielding to fantasy.

The Chinese per capita income in 1952 was one-fourth that of the Russians back in 1928, according to Walt W. Rostow, and since then it is reported to have dropped even lower.[41]

Some will say that China, like Russia, will always pose a military threat, no matter how internally weak it may be. A communist nation is so organized that an inner corps, dedicated to world domination, is likely to survive domestic unrest and economic disarray, and, surviving, maintain the military strength to continue the threat. Especially of a quick atomic war.

To this one can only reply that the military and economic strength of the United States for the immediate years ahead is so great that one must assume the threat of China is indeed spavined.

The political analysts pondering the future menace of China and also of Russia should first of all consider what the internal results would have been in those countries today if their military opponents had not shipped those huge amounts of grain to them during the last couple of years. The prospect is that the shipments will continue ever larger — until the member states of The Granary decide, for whatever reason, to stop them. When that happens rioting and civil disorder will surely be imminent behind the torn curtain.

# 7

## Suddenly, American Food "Surpluses" Are Gone. Where Now?

At an official function I met a White Russian lady who was the wife of a European diplomat. I had recently been in Vladivostok and she said her family had fled there during the earliest days of the Bolshevik Revolution, when World War I was drawing to a close and she was about twelve years old. She told of the city's occupation by American troops and said that her chief memory was the one good meal a day she received at her school from food supplied by the Americans.

Because of the continual accounts in the press today about how grateful the schoolchildren are around the world for the food being received from the Americans under the surplus food program, I could not resist asking if she felt grateful for having had American food when she was in school.

"Grateful? Oddly, I never thought of it that way," she said. "I suppose I should be deeply grateful, for I am sure it kept me in health for a whole year. Yet everything was so touch and go in those days. It wasn't only the food that we didn't have: it was also the clothing, heat, everything. Not even one extra little thing that could be called a luxury. No. I would say I am not at all grateful. The food appeared at the school each day and America as the source of it was too far away, too vague to be understood. Certainly, in all my married life in the various embassies, it never once entered my head that I ought to be more friendly or helpful to the Americans I meet because of the food I received during those days in Vladivostok. No, I have no feeling of gratitude or obligation. I don't know why. I suppose I should have."

No one knows how many people throughout the world now receive food each day from our "bountiful surplus." Even the officials of the program are unable to be precise. AID Director David Bell states that 70 million children receive this food daily.[1] This would make an understatement of the often-repeated figure of 100 million people a day, both adults and children. Norman Sklarewitz of the *Wall Street Journal* wrote that in India alone one out of every four persons receives this aid,[2] but his figure, totaling more than 120 million, must surely be too high. Also involved here is the quantity of food received per person. It probably seldom amounts to one full meal a day, American style, but is more in the nature of a supplement to the diet. Yet the school lunches are real enough as proper meals in comparison to what the children are accustomed to. Anyway, the one thing to which each and every one agrees: there are a lot of people eating a lot of American surplus food.

Whatever Americans may individually think of our AID program, whether favorably or unfavorably, their opinion of the shipments of our "surplus" food has been almost universally laudatory.

This program, initiated by Congress in 1954, has been known as P.L. 480. The image men of President Kennedy changed the name to "Food for Peace." In 1966 President Johnson tried to change the name to "Food for Freedom," but when Congress worked over his bill it refused to give up "Peace" — and that is the *official* name today. Just the same, when the President signed the bill at the Texas White House he called it the "Food for Freedom" bill and the executive branch has received instructions, without publicity, to do likewise. One harried press officer told me that his releases may have to be worded "Food for Freedom (Food for Peace)." Presumably, the acronym in Washingtonese will now be FFFFFP.

Since the title is so in danger of change, I have decided to retain, for my discussion here, the original, well-known name of P.L. 480.

The official figure for all United States aid through the years is $104 billion (as of this writing). Of this, $14.9 billion is P.L. 480 "surplus," [3] which is a big mound of food. Food has been sent to 130 countries and territories.

There are several reasons why the American public so uniformly praises this program, but the most basic one lies in the fortuitous word "surplus." No one feels he is getting hurt personally by sending the food abroad (although one cannot help wonder what is the opinion of the quiescent hungry ones within our own country).

When inaugurated, the concept of the program immediately found favor with the American public. For the most part, the food was given away without strings; the rest of it became bookkeeping entries as "sales" for local money. Much of this local money was then either given or loaned back to the local government at minimum terms. Everything was painless for everyone. Basically, it was pure charity. The receiver did little, if anything, in return. The giver felt good from his alms-giving.

After a few years this program changed due to various revisions by Congress. Outright gifts became a smaller part of P.L. 480 and the "sales" for foreign currencies increased. This did not alter, however, the felicitous reaction of the American public. Those who favored receiving something in return for the food were satisfied. Those who favored pure charity also remained satisfied because they realized these "sales" for local currencies will most probably end up as gifts, for reasons I point out later.

Now P.L. 480 is suddenly entering a new phase. The "surplus" food stocks are fast disappearing. Other sources of food must be found if the shipments to the hungry nations are to be continued. Thus, it becomes quite a different type of operation, a much more complex subject for both the congressmen and the public to comprehend.

In forecasting the Time of Famines this new development regarding P.L. 480 is vital because one must assume that future American shipments of food to the hungry will be carried forward within the framework of this same organization. The same structure of officials will continue in charge and many of today's staff will still be working for it in 1975. As the Time of Famines gathers momentum and pre-existing forms of organization are found inadequate, new policies and new laws will be adopted, but these, most likely, will be grafted merely onto the old trunk of the P.L. 480 staff. Of such is the permanency of bureaucracy.

Hence, the need for me to go back and review the factors that brought P.L. 480 into existence, to examine the sectors of the American public which have benefited from it and to note why these same sectors will now urge continuation of P.L. 480 even though the "surpluses" are ending.

## *The Purpose of P.L. 480 Was to Get Rid of an Agricultural Glut*

With the end of World War II American agricultural output did not slack off; rather, it swelled upward. This was due as much to the culmination of the long years of fruitful research as to the expansion of all agricultural facilities to meet wartime demand.

Soon the American wheat farmer, as an example, became fearful of the prospect of a downward trend of prices as the war-ravaged countries gradually revived their own wheat output and as the production of the other Granary countries mounted ever higher. On a free market the farmer would have responded by adjusting his acreage to produce smaller amounts. All the wheat grown would still have been consumed; it would not have been thrown away. One use awaiting expansion, for instance, would have been the chicken and cattle growers who, if prices were lower, would buy wheat as feed.

Congress decided to expand the already established system of pegging the prices of specific farm products artificially above what a competitive market would pay. This program, consisting of an assortment of laws, was begun away back in 1933.

The direct result of tampering with the age-old law of supply and demand was to encourage production of more wheat and other agricultural products than could be sold at the pegged prices. All grain that could not be sold at the artificial price was purchased by the government with taxpayers' money and put into storage bins where the storage charges (also paid by the government) mounted higher and higher as the government acquired ever more of the agricultural produce.

"Some people think that surpluses make price supports necessary. On the contrary, price supports make surpluses inevitable," Professor Don Paarlberg states. "England is in deficit supply with respect to eggs and has long imported them from Denmark. England undertook to support the price of eggs at a high level and created a surplus. . . . The United States, which supplies only a fraction of its wool needs, supported the price of wool and created a surplus. . . . France, which formerly imported wheat, supported prices at a high level and created a surplus. . . . A surplus follows a high support price like the night follows the day. . . . [This] is economic orthodoxy." [4]

As long as the taxpayers are willing to pay direct sums from the national treasury (and indirectly in the form of high consumer prices) in support of a favored group of producers, then a surplus in a commodity can be achieved.

By 1954 the crisis of glut had arrived. The United States was awash from the weight of agricultural "surpluses." We had then in storage 903 million bushels of wheat, 918 million bushels of corn, 9.7 million bales of cotton. This was the year they started to use the mothballed maritime fleet for storage. The total investment of the Commodity Credit Corporation (CCC) jumped in 1954 to $6 billion, in contrast to $3.4 billion in 1953. The legal borrowing limit of CCC had to be increased two times in 1954. [5]

Thus, Congress in 1954 was forced to take action of some kind as a result of the near breakdown of storage facilities (and the high costs of storage fees) for this burgeoning flood of foodstuffs. On the other hand, Congress was unwilling, for political reasons, to turn off the farmers' excessive production via the orthodox method of phasing out the price supports.

Accordingly, the 480th public law it passed that year provided for sending our "surplus" food direct to the hungry nations, government-to-government, no commercial channels involved. In an earlier day Brazil had handled a similar surplus of coffee by burning the stuff.

P.L. 480 thus was passed by Congress with the straight, dead-serious purpose of getting rid of our agricultural glut. Charity and other humanitarian ideas were not the moving force, as was indicated by the title of the Act itself: "The Agricultural Trade Development and Assistance Act." So that there is no doubt, I point out the word "Agricultural" referred *not* to the agriculture of the hungry nations but to that of the United States.

I here quote the introduction of the law which was also repeated unchanged upon each renewal since then, until replaced by the new Food for Peace Act of 1966 (I have added numbering to make it easier to read):

AN ACT To Increase the Consumption of United States Agricultural Commodities in Foreign Countries, To Improve the Foreign Relations of the United States, and for other Purposes. . . .

Sec. 2. It is hereby declared to be the policy of Congress

(1) To expand international trade among the United States and friendly nations,

(2) To promote the economic stability of American agriculture and the national welfare,

(3) To make maximum efficient use of surplus agricultural commodities in furtherance of the foreign policy of the United States,

(4) And to stimulate and facilitate the expansion of foreign trade in agricultural commodities produced in the United States by providing a means whereby surplus agricultural commodities in excess of the usual marketings of such commodities may be sold through private trade channels, and foreign currencies accepted in payment therefore.

(5) It is further the policy to use foreign currencies which accrue to the United States under this Act to expand international trade, to encourage economic development, to purchase strategic materials, to pay United States obligations abroad, to promote collective strength, and to foster in other ways the foreign policy of the United States.

The actual operation of the program was set forth in the following titles which provided the framework for the distribution of the food:

Title I — authorized the food to be sold for local currencies.

Title II — authorized the food to be used for disaster relief.

Title III — authorized the food to be given free to American voluntary agencies and international organizations for distribution through their private channels, such as to schools.

Title IV (added in 1961) — authorized the food to be sold for dollars on long-range terms, usually not requiring any initial payments and allowing repayment to last for forty years.

Recently, a friend of mine who once was an official of the Department of Agriculture reminisced about the time he had written the first draft of P.L. 480.

"I could see the possibility of the American Government controlling a couple of dozen countries through these free-food shipments. We could control them because the food gave us power over the cities. Admittedly, we could not physically control the countryside. But so what? It is the capital cities that determine what course these nations take month-to-month. In its simplest form this is how I foresaw these food shipments would work: A country with riots coming on could be controlled by letting our wheat ships sit outside the port like a carrot on a stick. A leader whom we considered dangerous would lose the support of the masses because everyone would know we were not going to unload the wheat if he became top man or even if the government in power went overboard to the communist left or to the junta right. We might not stop all riots and revolutions this way but we could keep a lot of them from starting."

Because the operation of P.L. 480 has not worked out in this way (and, of course, the law in the end was not written in this fashion), one can say this former official was naïve to think along these lines while drawing up his first draft — or perhaps one can say he foresaw what may be happening in the coming crises of the Time of Famines. Nevertheless, note that he, and presumably his superior officers, had been thinking of P.L. 480 both as a means to get rid of the food surpluses and as a tool to further American foreign and commercial policies. Charity for humanity was not a predominant factor.

Economically, P.L. 480 was a wise piece of legislation, provided one accepts the basic thesis that Congress should continue to allocate taxpayer funds to support artificial prices for the benefit of American farmers.

With respect to foreign affairs, it would seem to be a valid concept to use this food as an active tool to implement American policies abroad. Nevertheless, our government apparently has not so utilized it.

A reputed case, which I kept hearing about, concerned wheat said to have been used in the Chilean elections of 1964. The story went that in the election campaign the United States feared that the extreme leftist candidate would win over the moderately leftist candidate, Frei, and a huge amount of grain was sent in to keep down food prices, thus contributing to Frei's election. Trying to verify this story in the State Department, I was confronted with a horrified gasp that "We would never do anything like that!" And the statistics show that no undue amount was sent to Chile.

Just the same, when an extra shipment of food will result in election returns favorable to us, I consider this outcome a more valuable payment for our food than any signed agreement to pay cash (maybe!) twenty or forty years later.

In contrast to a hypothetical action policy like this, a "passive," quite deliberate use of P.L. 480 food has occurred in the conduct of our relations with Egypt. The United States has continued to ship to Egypt year after year large amounts (totaling over $1 billion) of P.L. 480 food, thereby, for a certainty, helping to maintain domestic order and to keep the masses quiet for the benefit of Nasser. During this time Nasser nevertheless has continued spasmodic anti-American propaganda and has instigated active subversions of American policies in the Middle East, the Congo and elsewhere.

"Diplomatic cables from the Near East report that Nasser is in a precarious political position, and that failure to get American grain would cause street riots, probably rebellion by the army, and his downfall." [6]

One can argue the United States has been foolish to buttress and shore up Nasser, an avowed enemy, but one assumes that the United States government has carried forward this policy after due deliberation in weighing the pros and cons. It could have cut off the P.L. 480 food at any time; instead, it continued to send the shipments as a tool in implementing its policy of restraint toward Nasser.

## But P.L. 480 Immediately Became Identified as "Humanitarian"

As soon as P.L. 480 became a law a metamorphosis took place in the public mind regarding it. Although the law was, remember, "The Agricultural Trade and Development Act," it came to represent a form of pure charity.

It is pertinent to point out that the foreign officials and general public in the receiving nations also accepted, quite naturally, this

American "humanitarian" viewpoint. Here, again, the fortuitous word "surplus" set the tone. At the Senate hearings for consideration of the proposed 1966 Food for Peace bill, Secretary of Agriculture Orville L. Freeman acknowledged that getting rid of the word "surplus" will change the attitude of the recipient countries. "When I have gone to these countries, the first thing I say at a press conference is, 'Look, the American farmers produce it and the taxpayers pay for it, and if you don't want it we won't send it.' . . . they now realize we no longer have the galloping surpluses. The whole philosophy of 'This is a surplus, we do you a favor by taking it' I think is eroding. . . ."

Senator B. Everett Jordan responded, "I talked to one of the members of the Parliament (in India) and he told me just exactly that. He said, 'It is cheaper to give it to us than it is to burn it. You have to get rid of it somehow.' . . . I said, 'Mister, who has been talking to you? The American taxpayer pays for that wheat.' He didn't believe it but I told him." [7]

Thus, the quite practical motives incorporated in the law faded into the background almost before the ink was dry on the President's signature. In the public mind the intent of the law became one to fulfill American obligations to mankind, help poor foreigners to stand erect, bring health to hungry children, give unto others as ye would have them give unto you in time of hunger. Such humanitarian aspects were, however, only a veneer added to a solid, useful piece of legislation incorporating the practical politics of 1954.

As far as Congress was concerned, moreover, the humanitarian aspects remained clearly subordinate to the effort to receive in return for the food some sort of foreign policy benefit — if only in the form of good will from the eaters. This is evidenced by Congress's instructions to tie the donations of food to various propaganda activities. *All* food shipped under Titles II and III of the law carries the sign in the local language, "Donated by the people of the United States of America." Thus, Congress wants these charity packages to generate credit where credit is due and for the receivers to repay their thanks, it trusts, with political friendliness or by buying our products.

Another phrasing of this aspect of humanitarianism is this:

I find it more admirable, more inspiring, to feed a starving child in South America than to obliterate a Russian in Murmansk. This is not sentimentality. A starving child is going to grow up to be a very real threat to my children. A well-fed one can be conned into becoming a lovely little consumer. We can sell him a washing machine. Or democracy.[8]

## What Have Been the Results of P.L. 480?

Some of the results are favorable and some, depending on one's economic outlook, are unfavorable.

### 1. Reduction of Storage Costs of Surplus Stocks

The cost of storing the "surplus" foodstuffs which the artificially pegged prices had produced rose in the peak year of 1960 to $576 million. When the Kennedy Administration began its effort to shove out P.L. 480 shipments to the utmost, the storage costs were reduced to $230 million in 1965 and they are still going down.[9]

### 2. Disposal of the Surpluses

In 1954 the burden of the annual increases of "surplus" food was truly oppressive. To dump these stocks onto the American market would have brought catastrophe to the farmers. To dump the stocks on the international market would have damaged the economies of several nations.

Today many of the products originally included in the P.L. 480 program have been withdrawn entirely because their "surpluses" have ceased to exist; their entire production is now marketed directly through normal commercial channels. The still remaining items labeled "surplus" are soon expected to decline to a level no higher than needed for an "ever normal" United States granary. Thus, the law has successfully disposed of our former glut of foodstuffs. In the meanwhile, it bought time for other economic factors gradually to evolve those conditions which now allow more farm production to mesh with the annual demand.

### 3. Maintenance of Prosperity of the Farmers

The farmers during all this period have remained a reasonably prosperous group on an overall basis. Without P.L. 480 disposing

of their excess production, Congress would have found it difficult
to maintain the price support program. If the program had been
canceled there might have been terrible hardships for the farmers,
as terrible as the near collapse of the farming community in 1921.

## 4. *Strengthening of the Private Distribution Agencies*

The non-profit agencies which have played such a major role in
the distribution of the food abroad have been directly helped.
CARE, for instance, probably would long since have reverted to a
minuscule operation without this source of food. The Red Cross
has been better able to send its crash relief to help alleviate various
world catastrophes. The religious organizations have been able to
expand far beyond their former scope of work in their chosen
countries.

The size of this work is indicated by the number of people they
feed with P.L. 480 food. In fiscal year 1965 CARE fed 35,484,000.
Catholic Relief Service fed 22,632,000. The approximately fifteen
other agencies combined, including UNICEF, Red Cross and religious groups, fed 9,249,000.[10]

Regarding CARE, note that in 1965 it received 877 million
pounds of P.L. 480 food donations in contrast to only 4 million
pounds of food contributed by private American citizens and foreign governments.[11]

## 5. *Effect on the Agricultures of the Receiving Nations*

Although it would be difficult to prove, some development specialists feel that P.L. 480 has discouraged the governments of certain of the hungry nations from giving full attention to improving
their own agricultures. These food shipments have too often enabled governments to coast along with their dreams of industrialization, dreams of international prestige and similar chimeras without the need to face up to their food crisis. Egypt would be an
example of this.

In 1964 I was in Rio de Janeiro and saw people lined up, sometimes for blocks, waiting to buy milk. The milk shortage in Rio is
chronic. Now, in addition, there was a strike of the commercial
milk producers. The same week I visited a primary school in Bra-
sília, the new capital in the interior. Like most other such schools

this had a clean, well-equipped kitchen, the chief use of which was to give American "surplus" milk to the children. I asked the teacher, "Where does the milk come from?" "Why, from Brazil, of course. We produce a lot of milk!" My reaction was not regret that my country was failing to receive credit for this gift; I was already used to that in many countries (despite the ever present American emblems on the packages). Rather, I could not help but think how difficult it would be for a Brazilian congressman to urge passage of a bill authorizing funds to study ways in which domestic milk production could be increased to satisfy national consumption. Other congressmen would say, "But we already produce a lot of milk. Our children receive it free in school."

Another aspect of the same problem illustrates how the artificial injection of our free food often creates a new problem and then another and another in a chain reaction. I quote from a letter to me from Warren H. Leonard, Professor of Agronomy, Colorado State University, who was a consultant to the World Bank in Libya in 1959:

Libya was self-sufficient in food for a short time during the British occupation after World War II when barley and dates were the principal staple foods. Wheat consumption has increased markedly since Libya became independent in 1952, but most of the wheat or flour has been imported in spite of good possibilities for increased wheat production in Libya by local farmers. Due to world surpluses, whole wheat could be shipped into Libya at a cost of 25 to 30 Libyan pounds per ton, while it cost an average of about 35 Libyan pounds for local Libyan farmers to produce a ton of wheat. As a result, wheat production in Libya was discouraged. Shipments of so-called "gift" wheat from the United States made the situation even worse. It should be pointed out that about 50 per cent of the domestic consumption of wheat in Libya (1955-58) was in the form of imported flour from Italy. This flour, largely made from U.S. gift wheat, was sold in Libya for a profit at a figure far below the cost of flour milled from local wheat. In fact, the largest flour mill in all Africa, located in Tripoli, was operating at only 10 per cent capacity when we were in Libya.[12]

## 6. *Increase in the Consumption of American Foods Abroad*

Remember, the first words of P.L. 480 read, "An Act to Increase the Consumption of United States Agricultural Commodities in

Foreign Countries. . . ." How much success in this respect has
been achieved is hard to pin down because so many psychological
factors are involved in changing the food tastes of a population.
Claiming success in this is, however, a major theme in P.L. 480
reports. Its representatives testify before Congress that a direct result of these food shipments is an important increase in commercial exports of American foods. In furthering these exports the
P.L. 480 officials are acting within the intent of the law. I do
protest, nevertheless, that there is another way of looking at this
aspect of P.L. 480. When these nations spend ever larger amounts
of their limited foreign exchange for new types of alien food, instead of knuckling down and increasing their local production of
food, this must surely be one factor in their continued failure to
*develop.*

Recently, I was in Fortaleza, a major port city in northeast Brazil
in the heart of the tropics. The poverty of the area's agriculture is
appalling. Most people say this is because it suffers from lack of
rainfall; my own opinion is that a still greater drawback to the area's
agriculture is the poor water-holding capacity of its soils. In any
case, this region has long been unable to feed its population. One
day I saw three American freighters lined up at the docks waiting
to unload their P.L. 480 wheat and I remembered a friend who had
told me of bread selling in the Congo for less than it does in the
United States, bread made entirely from P.L. 480 wheat and for
which the Congolese have now developed a great craving. I also
recalled the statement of another friend that the United States
government is tieing the tropics — such as the Congo and here in
Fortaleza — to our wheat production by creating a taste for raised
bread where before this was unknown. Of all the cereals only
wheat has gluten and without gluten bread dough will not make a
bubble and without a bubble the dough will not rise. But wheat
will not grow in the low tropics.

P.L. 480 wheat is indeed tieing the tropics to us in a most adverse fashion; it creates a new, artificial taste for a bulk product
which the region can never provide for itself.

While on the one hand we want the hungry nations to stand on
their own feet, clearly there are some who do not want them to
stand *too* firmly! Congressman Jamie L. Whitten, Chairman of the

House Subcommittee on the Department of Agriculture appropriations, told Secretary Freeman in 1966: "I think you should be very skeptical about any shift of Public Law 480 to the foreign aid group or to the State Department. Those of us who have been here as long as I have will recall that Public Law 480 was passed because the foreign aid group would not spend any foreign aid funds for American agricultural products. They were insistent that they set these foreign countries up in the business of producing, even when it was uneconomical in some instances." [13]

The interested American businessmen are quite honest and open in their concurrence with this thesis. Representatives of the National Milk Producers Federation stated in testimony before the Senate committee considering the 1966 Food for Peace bill, "The Government should plan with the milk-producing industry to carry on its activities in such a manner that markets once obtained through Public Law 480 can be retained." [14]

### 7. *Creation of a Mountain of U.S.-Owned Foreign Currencies ("Funny Money")*

By an odd quirk, our former unmanageable "surplus" of food at home has been replaced by an unmanageable "surplus" of foreign currencies abroad.

As P.L. 480 shipments leaped upward, the climate changed in Congress and stricter stipulations were imposed, requiring that more of the food be "sold," that is, that payment be received in local currency when conversion to dollars was not possible. This established the façade in Congress, and perhaps to the American public, that P.L. 480 is not just a giveaway program. Possibly the receiving government also benefited in its public relations at home because it was "paying its own way."

This system of United States–owned foreign currencies was devised before P.L. 480 was enacted. It would have remained a minor matter if the size of the food shipments had not been so large year after year and, in many countries, increased year after year. These are "soft" currencies because they cannot be exchanged into dollars. They can be spent only within the local country. Ergo, the popular nickname "funny money."

Senator Stuart Symington: ". . . we have nearly $3 billion of this foreign currency and I don't think one American in 10,000 knows we are locked up to that extent with all this foreign currency. If there is any hope of getting any of this currency back, I would hope we would try to do so; but I don't see how we can under the circumstances." [15]

In India the United States now owns title to two-thirds of all the currency that India has in circulation.[16]

The United States–owned foreign currencies were intended originally to be an easy way for the American government to pay for its assorted expenses in these countries, ranging from military matters to AID projects to constructing new embassy buildings to paying the expenses of visiting congressmen. But now it is out of hand.

" 'We've tried to find ways to use this money locally — such as to build or operate our embassies, but we just can't find enough ways to spend the stuff. It accumulates too fast! We have used all the money we can in every way we can,' a State Department official recently said. 'We are no longer making even a dent in the accumulation.' " [17]

Everyone concerned would like to use this money to develop the foreign country and enable its government to stand on its own feet. Unfortunately, for a variety of complex reasons, that is easier said than done. For example, if the United States just gives the "funny money" to the local government to spend outright, the increase in circulation would cause inflation. If the money were used to finance large development projects (like building a dam), then the local government would have to use so much foreign exchange to purchase abroad the necessary heavy equipment (bulldozers, construction steel, generators) that there would be little exchange left to cover the country's normal imports. When the United States loans this money back to the foreign government it finds that the interest payments, paid in local currency, simply increase the troublesome amount it already owns.

In the meantime the food keeps pouring into each country. The "funny money" becomes more difficult to use. Officials get more desperate to find projects on which to spend it.

Every indication is that the situation can be resolved in the end — when the political climate is right — only by canceling out all this money. Which is the reason I keep referring to the "free food" of P.L. 480, a term that today no official of the organization would accept as technically correct.

The postwar years have witnessed a remarkable effort by the rich nations to help the poor nations. This help, though, has been extended principally in long-term, low-interest loans, not in outright gifts. The result is a rapidly growing loan burden which already is beyond the abilities of most of the receiving nations to handle.

In the last ten years the external public debt of the developing countries has quadrupled to the point where now 12 per cent of their export earnings is needed simply to service the loans. The speed at which these service charges are snowballing is seen in the data for Latin America. The annual amount required to service the foreign indebtedness of Latin America (including amortization payments) is as follows:[18]

| 1956 | $ 455,000,000 |
| 1964 | 1,624,000,000 |
| 1965 | 2,100,000,000 |

By 1965 the charges on Latin America's foreign loans more than equaled the *total* annual foreign aid assistance envisaged when the Alliance for Progress was established in 1961.

The hungry nations not only are losing the capacity to feed themselves from their own production but also are losing, at an accelerating rate, the ability to pay for food from abroad.

## 8. *Effect on the Population Statistics*

There is also the indirect consequence of the effect of this food on the population explosion statistics of these countries. I am sure it is quite impossible for anyone to make an estimate as to how many people are alive today, who otherwise would have died, because of this food. Probably, the figure would be small because the food normally is given only to supplement the local diet so as to lessen malnutrition.

To the degree that P.L. 480 has brought some health to the people of these countries it can be said that the population explosion has been correspondingly enhanced. If one believes that this explosion should be curbed, not increased, then P.L. 480 has had an adverse effect. However, if one accepts the thesis that proper measures to cope with the population explosion can be taken by a citizenry only when it is healthy in body and mind, then perhaps the food shipments have been helpful — but where have the citizens used this alleged gift of health in order to battle the population explosion?

### 9. *Stimulation of the Feeling of Responsibility by American Citizens Toward the Hungry Nations*

The years of propaganda as to the happiness which P.L. 480 has brought to the suffering has surely been a major factor in focusing the attention of the American public on the problems of the undeveloped world. As a result, our government has had a genuine depth of support and understanding in its efforts to aid these nations.

I call it propaganda, for that is what it actually has been. However, it has also been a program of education in the best sense of the word. Without it the American public would today be less knowledgeable about the problems of the world and less able to understand America's responsibility in world affairs. It has been a tangible factor in keeping at bay the unworkable postulates of isolationism.

To summarize, P.L. 480 accomplished what Congress wanted it to do. It reduced our agricultural surpluses while increasing our foreign markets.

It has resulted also in a number of things that Congress had not anticipated. Not only did it produce an unmanageable pile of "funny money" but it so affected the internal economies of many of the hungry nations that few people can agree on just what has been the overall result of P.L. 480 on the development plans of those countries we want to help.

An additional result of P.L. 480 not included in the preceding list is one which clearly was not visualized in the original bill. For good or bad P.L. 480 created the present widespread campaign that America has the *obligation* to use its agricultural capacity to feed the world (and the receivers, too, quickly agreed that America has this obligation). Thus, while the initial purpose of the law has been accomplished and, therefore, the bill should have been expected to end with the cessation of "surpluses," this thesis of *obligation* to use our maximum agricultural capacity for the benefit of the world now has become a dominant influence in our foreign aid planning.

## The Non-Dead End of P.L. 480

A few experts may have foreseen several years ago, the end of the United States agricultural "surpluses." For most officials, however, it has come as a shock that these American farm bounties are rapidly vanishing.

"We now expect that within a few years available stocks of most agricultural commodities will have declined to a level no higher than needed for an 'ever-normal granary.' It is therefore no longer possible to envisage an effective program of food aid based on surplus commodities." [19]

Credit is due the P.L. 480 officials for their success in efficiently disposing of the "surpluses" year after year by means of their larger and larger shipments to the hungry nations. However, P.L. 480 alone is not the cause of the "surpluses" coming to an end.

The abnormal postwar years are now merging into a level of normalcy as the recovered economies of western Europe and Japan once again become major markets for our farm products. The United States currently has a $6 billion trade surplus a year and two-thirds of this cushion for our economy is earned from farm exports.[20] In addition, the population of the United States has increased while also upgrading its diet. Thus, it consumes more of its own agricultural production.

"Surpluses" are nearly gone. Without "surpluses" P.L. 480 as originally conceived has no reason to exist.

In theory, the United States government should not be concerned about the closing down of P.L. 480. Since the original objective of disposing of the "surpluses" has been achieved, there should be no need for the Department of Agriculture to urge the law's continuation. True, if P.L. 480 were suddenly canceled, "surpluses" would begin to build up again. On the other hand, it should be reasonably easy, with the experience we now possess with acreage allotments, to scale production to our rising domestic and commercial export needs. Thus, the Department of Agriculture boys should pat the P.L. 480 boys on the back for a job well done and let P.L. 480 die with laurels for its successful career.

Nor should the State Department object to the demise of P.L. 480 inasmuch as it rarely used the food shipments as an instrument of foreign policy. The best that can be said for these shipments is that in a few countries they decreased tensions and unrest (as in India and Egypt). Yet it is unlikely that the international policies of any of the receiving countries were altered one whit because of the food.

Secretary of State Dean Rusk has testified: "I would like to stress, Mr. Chairman, that our food aid program has been a valuable foreign policy tool because it is directed toward positive changes — strengthening democratic governments, promoting political stability, encouraging economic stability, assisting national development." [21]

These are vague claims. It would be useful to have them reduced to specific examples of specific cases. Until this is done my earlier observation that P.L. 480 has not been used by the State Department as a tool in foreign policy maneuvers must remain unaltered.

Despite these reasons for letting P.L. 480 die a natural death, a campaign for a new concept, a new law, to replace the old one was begun in early 1965. The campaign resulted in the enactment of a new Food for Peace bill in 1966. As a substitute for the vanishing "surpluses" this new bill adopted the concept that the American farmers now should grow extra crops specifically for feeding the hungry world.

I interpolate here, before describing this campaign for increased acreage, that some experts doubt that this new concept will enable the new program to catch up with the ever mounting demand for grain. Karl Hobson of Washington State University: "I believe that even if we let all the idled land from government programs come back into production we probably would be hardly able to detect a ripple in production of major farm products — just as we were unable to see any ripple at all when the Soil Bank program idled millions of acres." [22]

Nevertheless, the expansion of production by bringing back into use the presently idled land of the United States may result in an important new psychological shift within American farm and political circles.

Of particular interest are the activists who prepared the groundwork of this campaign for the new Food for Peace bill and who lobbied its passage. They formed specific, clearly defined groups, inside and outside the government. They had a direct, personal interest that the old P.L. 480 not only be continued but be expanded beyond the current level of mammoth free-food programs. These groups were: (1) the humanitarians, (2) the businessmen, and (3) the development bureaucracy.

## The Humanitarians

The twelve years of P.L. 480 generated a new type of advocate who looks upon this program as the mechanism with which America must meet its "obligation" to the hungry world. This highly motivated, highly altruistic group is a hallmark of our age. With starving people in the world they cannot visualize their country not extending maximum help. This group has, therefore, not only reinforced what should be a weak interest of the Departments of State and Agriculture in the continuation of P.L. 480 but in 1966 also created and led the campaign to expand the entire program with a new Food for Peace bill.

This group, whom I call the humanitarians, claims that Americans have a moral obligation in this affair. I say "affair" because I am not sure how to word this. It is one thing to say that we have a humanitarian, moral obligation to share our "surpluses" with the hungry nations, but with these "surpluses" gone it would seem that there would be no further obligation. We could then let the age-old law of supply and demand once again regulate our farmers' production. At least, I recall no one ever seriously claiming that Americans had such an obligation in the days before P.L. 480. Nor do I hear these same advocates say that Canada, Australia and Argentina have a similar obligation. Only us.

The humanitarians have become an extremely powerful group and their influence in controlling the future of Food for Peace should not be minimized. I point out also that this influence is not one of simple spontaneity or of disinterested good will. Consider, for instance, what P.L. 480 did materially in behalf of the leading components of this group.

The 1964 Annual Report on Public Law 480 listed the following

non-profit American agencies which distributed the food donations
that year. These were:[23]

> CARE
> Catholic Relief Service
> Church World Service
> UNICEF
> Lutheran World Relief
> American Jewish Joint Distribution Committee
> American Mission to Greeks
> American National Red Cross
> American Relief for Poland
> Foreign Service Committee — Assemblies of God
> Hadassah, Inc.
> Mennonite Central Committee
> National Association of Evangelicals, World Re-
>     lief Commission
> People to People Health Foundation
> Seventh-day Adventist Welfare Service
> United Nations Relief and Works Agency
> Volunteer Border Relief

Although the first two on the list, CARE and Catholic Relief
Service, received five-sixths of the total, the activity of all these
agencies and groups has been greatly expanded because of their
distribution work. In 1965 it permitted them to give food to over
67 million people in the hungry nations. For both the people receiving the food and the agencies themselves P.L. 480 has been, in
a most literal sense, a godsend.

Add up the United States citizens represented by these agencies
and you have a huge constituency advocating this distribution of
our food abroad, a constituency that has access to every senator and
representative. The cumulative effect of these agencies has been a
continuously favorable publicity barrage in all the media. At congressional hearings they are eager witnesses. In the halls outside
they are active lobbyists.

I do not protest nor do I feel it wrong that these agencies lobby
in behalf of P.L. 480 and Food for Peace. Of such is today's way of
life in the laic and the cleric worlds. Also I have watched these
agencies distribute the food in a dozen countries from Jordan to
Brazil to the Dominican Republic to Laos. In each case which I

have observed the agency has handled the distribution honestly and the personnel have been truly dedicated.

Nevertheless, the self-interest of these agencies must be recognized in order to understand the motivation for their lobbying. When the life of P.L. 480 was in jeopardy in 1966 they most definitely had a vested interest (both material and moral) in having the program continued and expanded.

The world's humanitarians are a vital force and I hope there will always be such a group actively worrying about mankind. However, their role on behalf of Food for Peace should not be blurred to the public by their humanitarian adjectives. Out of the highest of ideals and with the most humane objectives they urged that the productive capacity of America's farms be expanded to the utmost because we have, or so they say, this brand-new *obligation* to feed the world's hungry.

## The Businessmen

The humanitarians were joined in their campaign for a new Food for Peace bill by a wide variety of special economic groups who quickly saddled on to this good horse in order to further their own self-interests. Nor does this mean they were joining in hypocritically; I accept that they are as sincere in their worry for mankind as the humanitarians. Nevertheless, because these special groups adopted the same adjectives as the humanitarian group one finds the resultant combination a tremendously powerful lobby bloc.

I attended the organizational meeting of the Committee on the World Food Crisis, which includes many of these interested people. The Committee's purpose was to organize (to lobby) congressional interest to expand P.L. 480 into the new Food for Peace act. Throughout the meeting the turgid oratory pleaded for the United States not to turn its back on the opportunity to share American abundance with the hungry, the downtrodden and the helpless of the world. In this sort of atmosphere I welcomed the unadorned statement of Governor William H. Avery of Kansas.

After taking note of the humanitarian overtones of the previous oratory, he said "Hard, cold economic facts may be a little out of place . . . [but] economic consequences can not be pushed aside and overlooked." He then listed certain American business groups who had benefited directly from P.L. 480 and who will, therefore, use their influence to have the restrictions removed from our farmers so that food shipments will continue and expand.

"The common carrier on water or land," he said, "has his rates fixed, and therefore would logically favor this production concept because it translates into more business.

"The manufacturer of farm machinery will want to sell more equipment and probably at increased prices.

"The fertilizer industry will favor the program because fertilizer is needed to produce a profitable crop in virtually all regions of the nation.

"Financial interests will be willing to extend credit, as there is every evidence that agriculture is moving into a cycle of the seller's market and, therefore, the loan is a good risk." [24]

The business magazine *Forbes* published an article which the cover featured, "Feeding the World's Hungry Millions: How it will mean billions for U.S. business." The article emphasized the wide range of American companies which expect to benefit directly from the expansion of American farming as a result of sending the charity food abroad. A few companies are planning to build branch plants in the hungry nations. However, most of the profits will come directly from inside the American boundaries by selling the output to the United States government. The article listed forty-three American companies, many among the largest in the country, which "will help feed the world." These were grouped under "Fertilizer Producers," "Agricultural Equipment," "Food Processors," "Construction," and "Grain-Carrying Railroads." [25]

Removing controls from the farmers in order to increase production for the world's hungry will result in a lot of profits for a lot of entrepreneurs.

Which is all right.

Except that it attracts the flies.

James G. Patton, president of the National Farmers Union, already has carried to its next logical step the concept of farming specifically in behalf of the poor of other nations. He urged that the food aid concept "needs to be extended to include the sale of farm machinery, steel, cement, fertilizer and other production items we have the capacity to produce." [26]

By "sale" I assume he means sale by the United States government to the undeveloped nations for "funny money" — which surely will some day be canceled out in red ink the same as were most of our World War I loans. Nevertheless, the manufacturers of the farm machinery, steel, cement, fertilizer, etc., etc., will, need I add, insist on hard dollars from the United States Treasury before releasing their products to this "humane" program.

Thus, in addition to producing food for "sale" under the most dubious of terms, we may find ourselves also sending manufactured goods in the same ships carrying the Food-for-Peace food.

Congressman Harold D. Cooley, Chairman of the House Committee on Agriculture and representative in charge of the hearings for enactment of the 1966 Food for Peace bill, eloquently claimed, "Food and fiber are weapons of peace. These weapons in our hands must be unsheathed. . . . The world cries out for food and fiber." [27] Letting fiber ride the coattails of this food program caught me a bit by surprise, but then I am not from Congressman Cooley's cotton-picking Fourth District of North Carolina and can be forgiven for not hearing before that the United States has the obligation to feed *and* clothe the needy ones of the world.

## The Development Bureaucracy

Finally, a third group should be added to the humanitarians and the business associations who advocated the continuation and expansion of P.L. 480 into Food for Peace. These are the government officials who have risen within the bureaucracy via our aid programs. As a result of a quarter of a century of foreign aid effort by the United States, the United Nations and the foundations (and the resultant proliferation of university professors teaching development courses), the 1950's saw the birth of a new category of professional men: the Economic Development Experts. By now their number seems legion! The new profession already has its own trade association, the Society for International Development. Although this includes only a portion of the professionals, it has over four thousand members! Generally speaking, one can say that a man who has worked for five years or longer with a development agency has become one of this corps of professional men and is deeply interested in furthering the scope of his profession.

Thus, when they appear as witnesses in congressional hearings one must accept that they are biased, even though sincerely so, in favor of a continuation of the principle of P.L. 480. When they testify as to the GNP of Zambia and Malaysia, the inputs and outputs that control the economies of Colombia and Iran, the need of India and Paraguay for fertilizer, the need of The Gambia for cheaper peanut processing, they sound like technicians thinking solely of technical problems. Yet they are career men. If the government money for which they are so sincerely and honestly campaigning were to end, their new careers would receive a serious blow. As a member of this profession myself, I know the sincerity of the group. I, too, cannot conceive of a future world in which the United States will not extend help to the undeveloped.

In 1965 I attended a work session at Estes Park arranged by the Rockefeller Foundation and P.L. 480 to suggest ideas on "Whither P.L. 480?" The group was a distinguished, across-the-board range of specialists who for five days discussed the various aspects of the vanishing "surpluses." Always, however, the discussion was couched in humanitarian terms with no one doubting or questioning the moral obligation of the United States to feed the hungry nations. A priori this was accepted. The conclusions of the meeting, need it be said, were that the American farmer should be "turned loose" to feed the world and that P.L. 480 should be expanded far beyond the limits of all its previous activities.

Thus, while the reasons for which P.L. 480 was written no longer exist, no one that I know about argued at the congressional hearings to let the law die. In 1966 the new Food for Peace passed with a resounding voice vote in the House and a 72-to-2 vote in the Senate. Congress authorized a $7.4 billion food aid bill — the largest in the country's history!

There is too large a head of steam built up ever to see this program die in our generation. Too many people favor its continuation to allow political Washington to ignore politics and the lobbyists and their constituencies.

# The "Self-Help" Fallacy of the New
# Food for Peace

The formal campaign for a "new" Food for Peace bill to replace and even to expand the old P.L. 480 was initiated in February 1966 when President Johnson sent to Congress his "War on Hunger" message. In it he proposed the elimination of the "surplus" concept in food aid and the substitution of "expanded food shipments to countries where food needs are growing and self-help efforts are under way." [1]

The elimination of the "surplus" concept from P.L. 480 was, of course, inevitable for the obvious reason that the "surpluses" are disappearing.

The substitution of the "self-help" motif was underlined as the President called for sending food to those countries where "self-help efforts are under way." In fact, he referred to "self-help" five times, making it the key phrase in his message. The nation's press rightly adopted the term for its headlines.

"Self-help," however, was not defined. The term was left to hang in mid-air, that is, to speak for itself with all its upstanding connotations of thrift and independence and git-up-and-go. The President implied that earlier food shipments under P.L. 480 had gone to countries that were not prepared to cooperate with "self-help," but that success in the future would be achieved because shipments now would be sent only to those countries willing to initiate "self-help."

I was curious where President Johnson had acquired this augury of "self-help." A clue came two weeks later when the Secretary of Agriculture, Orville L. Freeman, testified before the House Committee on Agriculture. He referred again to the same Department of Agriculture report I previously criticized in Chapter 2, "Changes in Agriculture in 26 Developing Nations, 1948 to 1963."

"Twelve out of the twenty-six have increased their agricultural production at annual compound rates of more than 4 per cent per year. This surpasses rates ever achieved by the now economically advanced nations over comparable periods of time. . . . They had only one factor in common — *a national determination to carry out self-help policies to improve their food production.*" [2] The italics are mine.

I telephoned a friend who had worked on the "26 Nations" study, and asked, "Where did the Secretary get this self-help angle?" The friend replied that the documentation for the Secretary's testimony was to be found in the following statement from this same study:

. . . evidence as is available, however, shows that rapid rates of increase in crop output have not just been a consequence of normal economic and social processes in societies organized on a laissez-faire basis. Rather, they have been undergirded by aggressive group action — generally national in scope — which has been directed specifically to improving agricultural service facilities.[3]

My comment was, "That doesn't mean a thing except to claim that laissez-faire and free enterprise do not work. Do you really want to admit that? In any case," I added, "whatever one may think of the principle of laissez-faire, how can this be interpreted as having anything to do with self-help?"

My friend said, "I can't interpret for the Secretary. I suppose that anything a nation does is self-help. If it builds a road, that's self-help. If it stabilizes the market price, that's self-help. If it uses some fertilizer, that's self-help. I guess 'self-help' is a sort of catchphrase that serves a propaganda purpose in today's political atmosphere."

Since the administration could not use farm surpluses to justify continuing P.L. 480 and since our former food aid had not succeeded in making the hungry world less hungry, something new was needed to justify the new Food-for-Peace program. "Self-help" became the slogan.

If I were to ask you to buy a gem which to your untrained eye could be either a diamond or glass, you would demand proof the gem is real.

Similarly, the administration assumed that Congress would demand proof that the "new" Food for Peace would produce tangible, real results which in the past were not achieved under P.L. 480. Hence, the sudden bringing forward of "self-help" as "proof" of new criteria to be used by the bureaucracy. In his message the President said, "There is one characteristic common to all those [countries] who have increased the productivity of their farms: *a national will and determination to help themselves.*" [4] The italics are the President's.

In my opinion, the "self-help" proof that the diamond of the new Food for Peace is not glass has not been presented. It may sound logical that a nation succeeds in moving its agricultural mountains when it has a "national determination to carry out self-help policies" but the proof has not been demonstrated.

There is, of course, much more to attaining agricultural self-sufficiency than just a will to succeed. A nation must have the right combination of soil and climate, to name the most obvious. Also, the population pressures must not be so oppressive that the resources at hand are unable to supply the required food.

After twelve years P.L. 480 was too firmly established in the bureaucracy (and in various sectors of the American economy) to be allowed a natural death. The cessation of "surpluses" did force, however, a new arrangement of words, a new dress, in order to retain public and congressional support. The fervid phrases of the humanitarians were not enough to justify the continuation of the program, even when voiced by the President, as in his message to Congress: "When men and their families are hungry . . . the world is restless. . . . Hunger poisons the mind. It saps the body. It destroys hope. It is the natural enemy of every man on earth." [5]

No one, least of all me, can deny the sincerity underlying these humanitarian phrases. Yet there is an artificial ring to them because they seem to be used to "sell" Congress on continuing its authorization for the United States to feed the hungry world. The "self-help" slant now brought forward sounds like a sales gimmick with which to pressure Congress into believing that the P.L. 480 bureaucracy will stop distributing the food as planlessly as in the past.

Under the chairmanship of Harold D. Cooley, the House Committee on Agriculture began hearings on the Food for Peace bill shortly after receipt of the President's "War on Hunger" message. In the three volumes of testimony these hearings produced I found no instance of anyone's questioning the validity of the President's statement that those countries which had succeeded in developing their agricultures successfully possessed some special mystique called "a national determination to carry out self-help policies." Indeed, no one even asked for a definition of "self-help."

On the other hand, this question was raised constantly: What will the new bill do that the old P.L. 480 did not do? *

CONGRESSMAN POAGE: Tell us how this new bill is different from the present law. What new concepts are involved in it? [6]

CONGRESSMAN ABERNETHY: What is it that we will do under the Food for Freedom program that we are not actually doing right now? [7]

CONGRESSMAN COOLEY: We ought to know what . . . would be accomplished by the last bill that will not be accomplished by the first bill. [8]

CONGRESSMAN POAGE: I have gone through [the President's special food aid message] but I have not been able to find out just what improvements there would be. . . . What is new about it? [9]

The answers of the witnesses failed, however, to present details which would offer valid hope that our food aid would bring about changes in the agricultures of the hungry nations. The answers merely stressed that the new bill would remove the limitation of shipping "only surplus" commodities and, therefore, would allow our farmers to produce more for shipment overseas. The "new ap-

* Three volumes of testimony were printed for the House Agriculture Committee's hearings on this bill (the Senate's hearings were almost as extensive). For simplicity in presenting the tenor of these hearings I have confined all quotations in this chapter, except as noted otherwise, to the three days when Secretaries Freeman and Mann (who appeared for Secretary Rusk) and AID Administrator Bell were called before the House committee, February 23, 24, 25, 1966.

proach" with the receiving countries was simply a re-enunciation of what already has been tried for the past twelve years under the old P.L. 480.

CONGRESSMAN POAGE: I note that the Secretary refers to . . . "an opportunity for the new concepts on the use of food." . . . What are these new concepts?

UNDERSECRETARY OF STATE MANN: . . . self-help . . . higher priority for agricultural development . . . more sales of our products for dollars.[10]

CONGRESSWOMAN MAY: What is your thinking on how we might go about acquiring this self-help and how do we determine that nations are living up to whatever self-help criteria you may set up?

SECRETARY OF AGRICULTURE FREEMAN: We have given a great deal of thought to this. And like many important questions it does not lend itself to any easy or all-embracing answer.[11]

CONGRESSMAN FINDLEY: During the last year we have authorized three big shipments of commodities to India. Can you tell me what measures of self-help were imposed as a part of the agreements under which these shipments were made?

FREEMAN: We did not level a gun at India's head and say, "Because you had a drought and there is a danger of 50 million people starving, to get you either to do this or that or else you starve." . . . It is the whole new emphasis on agriculture . . . and we feel that the program is a good one and that it is being attacked with zest and with energy and we are very hopeful of the results.

FINDLEY: In other words, India is now doing all we can expect her to do in terms of self-help?

FREEMAN: It might not be $99\frac{44}{100}$ per cent pure. . . . It represents very significant progress.[12]

CONGRESSMAN FINDLEY: Can you tell us what measures of self-help India has agreed to in recent months in order to build up its own capacity for food production?

MR. BELL, ADMINISTRATOR FOR AID: The Indian Government has, in fact, changed its policy very sharply in [two] very important aspects. No. 1 . . . They have set out to make . . . internal prices . . . effective incentives for farmers to produce more.

FINDLEY: Can you give us that in terms of percentage price increase?

BELL: I do not recall. . . . My vague recollection is of the order of 25 per cent [record was later corrected to show it was 15 per cent]. . . . Point No. 2, the Indian Government . . . recognized that changeover in output . . . will come from using more fertilizer. . . . They have, also, taken . . . steps in the agricultural credit field . . . and are supporting rapid action to introduce and test new varieties, both of rice and of several other crops.[13]

CONGRESSMAN POAGE: The argument has been brought before us . . . that we are going to require more of the recipient countries in the way of self-help. . . . You must have something in mind that we are going to require of these people. What do you have in mind that we are going to require, particularly of India?

UNDERSECRETARY OF STATE MANN: Currency of India is overvalued. . . . Greater priority should be given to the private sector. . . . Much higher priority . . . for agriculture. . . . This would include a whole range of measures, stepping up the production of fertilizer and many other things. Those are three, from memory, Mr. Poage, that I remember offhand. There are one or two others.

POAGE: You are permitted to do that now; you can do all those things. You have that power from the very day when the [original] bill was passed, have you not?

MANN: I think that is correct, sir.[14]

CONGRESSMAN BELCHER: Under Public Law 480 have we been disposing of about all of the commodities that we could?

SECRETARY FREEMAN: Yes.

BELCHER: Under Public Law 480 we can do the same thing that we can do under this program, can't we?

FREEMAN: The new program represents an expansion both in concept and in resources over what we have had in the past.

BELCHER: I thought that we had been getting rid of about all that we possibly could in both types of programs.[15]

Throughout all the questioning of the key witnesses the congressional committee was never able to find out what was new about "self-help." They did learn, though, that there is nothing contemplated for the future that had not been tried in the past or was not authorized under the old P.L. 480. Even in the crucial area of increasing the quality and quantity of agricultural technicians needed to help the hungry nations learn to feed themselves no real change is contemplated.

CONGRESSMAN COOLEY: All of the ten experts that testified here last week emphasized that one point through all of their testimony, that we could not feed the world, but we could help them with some technicians, to give them people with know-how and show-how.[16]

CONGRESSWOMAN MAY: They anticipated that Asia and Latin America could effectively use between 5,000 and 10,000 agricultural specialists.[17]

CONGRESSMAN DOLE: Every one of the 10 public witnesses who appeared before the committee thus far stressed the need for more technical assistance. . . . Mr. Bell . . . pointed out that we have . . . not in excess of 1,000 technicians in foreign countries under the AID programs.[18]

CONGRESSMAN STALBAUM: Mr. Secretary [Freeman], I note that your message was rather sketchy on technical assistance. As Congressman Dole has pointed out — there is really no reference in the bill that you have brought to us in this regard.[19]

As I followed the testimony and talked with those charged with formulating the "new" Food for Peace bill, one thing became clear: there is no evidence that United States food aid under the "new" program will be, even slightly, more effective in improving agricultural conditions in the hungry nations than was the old P.L. 480 during the past twelve years.

And how effective has been that aid so far? Secretary Freeman testified: "The world situation in terms of food needs is much more alarming today than it was 12 years ago."[20] That is to say, before the shipment abroad of the $14.9 billion of P.L. 480 food.

Knowing today's agricultural failures in the hungry world and knowing what the administration is now proposing for the future, I see no possibility of the "new" Food for Peace bill preventing, or even minimizing, the coming of the Time of Famines.

To me the evidence at hand shows that AID Administrator Bell was not correct when he said, "Looking ahead, say, to the order of magnitudes for 5 or 10 years, we should see the beginnings of catching up with the food gap because of increases in local food production."[21]

Similarly, I find Secretary Freeman's statement a supposition without proof: "[If President Johnson's recommendations] are adopted, and if the developing nations will do their part, the trends that forecast the dark shadow of famine can be reversed." [22]

Congress passed the "new" Food for Peace bill and approved its $7.4 billion price tag despite the lack of evidence that it will change, not in the slightest, the agricultural decline in the hungry nations.

Too many groups of Americans profit from this program to allow the bill to be voted down, as illustrated by these excerpts from the same congressional testimony:

SECRETARY FREEMAN: Paradoxical as it may seem, agricultural development in the poor and hungry nations offers us the best opportunity for expanding exports of the products of our farms and factories.[23]

CONGRESSMAN POAGE (from cotton-producing Texas): What would be the attitude of the State Department if we provided a condition in our next agreement with India, that is, that we required as a condition for the shipment of additional American food to India that they remove from production a portion of their cotton acreage? [24]

CONGRESSMAN DOLE: I happen to represent the largest wheat producing district in the country. . . . We do not want everybody to stop eating wheat in these foreign countries. I . . . want to put in a plug for the wheat producers of America.[25]

CONGRESSMAN COOLEY: Another suggestion is that we try to get them to eat corn instead of wheat and rice. We have more corn than we have rice and wheat. A lot of people do not like cornbread, but I come from a cornbread country and I would rather have it than wheat bread. Cornpone is quite a dish down home.[26]

\*    \*    \*

CONGRESSMAN COOLEY: The bill that I introduced . . . was to strike out the word "surplus" in Public Law 480, so that we could produce food for distribution abroad, to take care of the hungry and the starving throughout the world. Of course, no one is advocating doing away with present restrictions on limitations on production *at the present time*.[27] [Italics are mine.]

How long is "at the present time"? Can we expect that once the camel's nose is under the tent and the concept established for

American farmers intentionally to produce food for distribution
abroad, to take care of the hungry and the starving throughout the
world, the camel will not crawl inside and most crop restrictions be
removed? In May 1966, two months after the testimony quoted
above, the same House committee approved raising the ceiling on
food shipment subsidies 30 per cent to $3.3 billion yearly.[28] The
chairman of this committee, Mr. Cooley, spoke at a meeting of the
Fertilizer Industry Advisory Panel in reference to the proposed
Food for Peace bill, saying:

> I can see millions of acres of our fertile lands coming out of retire-
> ment back into production.
> I can see Rural America flourishing again.
> I can see billions of dollars in goods crossing the seas.
> I can see the greatest surge in commercial trade the world has ever
> known.
> I see our industry booming along with our agriculture, and such
> growth in our own economy that every man who has the will to work
> may prosper for himself and his family, in productive and rewarding
> employment.[29]

Who can vote against such a program for Utopia? Does it make
much difference that there is no evidence to back up the hopes
aroused in the congressman's next statement: "Most of all I see
hunger obliterated from this world for every man willing to sweat
for his daily bread — where only those starve who are able but unwilling to work — and in all this I see the promise of a world
finally at peace." [30]

It is clear that some form of food aid to the hungry nations is
with us for all the foreseeable future. Such a program is now a
*permanent* part of our American political scene, a permanent part
of our economy.

Because this is so, it is important for the leaders in Washington
to forge the program into a useful, effective tool in order to further
the welfare of both the United States and of the world as a whole.

For myself, I am glad this program is a permanent part of our
American life.

I object, however, to the dead-end direction which the program
now is taking under the banner of "self-help." It is, in my opinion,
wasteful to expand "food shipments to countries where food needs

are growing and self-help efforts are under way," to repeat the President's words. It is a scattering of a valuable asset of the American people. It is a squandering of resources that should be a heritage for our children.

My objection arises out of this new, quite insidious catch-phrase of "self-help." It implies that these nations to whom we plan to ship an open-end, *permanent* outpouring of our agricultural produce can get their agricultural houses in order if they would only roll up the sleeves, knuckle down and stop goofing off on the job. Seldom, in fact, has a world power insulted its friends so blatantly.

For these nations already are trying, each in its own fashion, to get their economies to grow. They are already knee-deep in the frustrations of "self-help" arising from lack of modern techniques. What they are doing may be wrong and they may be emphasizing the wrong things in their development plans, but certainly the efforts can rightly be labeled "self-help."

To tie our food aid to the thesis of "self-help" will end up by our giving food to *every* nation. Such a propaganda phrase offers no guideline as to how Food for Peace officials should attempt to separate those countries which are *able* to get their agricultures moving in order to ameliorate the shock of food shortages from those countries which are *not* able.

There are many nations for whom our food can be a valuable aid as they strive to make themselves agriculturally more self-sufficient. There are others, however, for whom the hour of overpopulation has knelled. For them our food shipments are now too late to stimulate their resources in time to deflect the famines. "Self-help" is indeed a cloudcuckooland criterion to use in determining how to allocate effectively our limited food stocks.

Today, we have food programs in over one hundred countries.[31] Under the tinsel banner of "self-help" we shall probably continue to have the same old food programs in these same one hundred nations.

By 1975 many of these hundred countries will have lost the capability, even with massive American food aid, to feed themselves. By continuing planlessly to send our food to all we stretch thin our food stocks to the point that few, and probably none, of the endangered nations can be truly protected and saved during the Time of Famines.

Therein lies the fallacy of the "new look" in Food for Peace. It tries to separate countries that would like to become self-sufficient in food production from those that would not. But where, in the latter category, does such a country exist in the whole wide world?

Our food aid should, instead, distinguish between those which are *able*, if given help, to ride out the storm of the Time of Famines from those which are *not* able.

The difference between "would like" and "able" is the difference between failure and success in the disposition of our food resourees.

PART ☐☐☐

# Potential Role of the United States During the Time of Famines

> Famine, like hanging, concentrates attention wonderfully.
>
> BERNARD D. NOSSITER

# ⑨

## *Herewith Is a Proposal for the Use of American Food: "Triage"*

I now propose a course of action which I believe to be a feasible procedure to achieve maximum benefits from the distribution of our food stocks, both for the United States and for the world as a whole. It is my alternative to an unplanned escalation of food aid, an alternative to an aimless frittering away of this precious food resource. It requires no new law but can be carried out under the existing Food for Peace bill.

To summarize what I have emphasized in earlier chapters:

(*a*) The exploding populations in the hungry nations combined with their static agricultures make famines, in many, inevitable. Their future contains a mounting increase of civil tensions, riots and military take-overs as the growing scarcity of food forces prices higher and higher.

(*b*) The timetable of food shortages will vary from nation to nation, but by 1975 sufficiently serious food crises will have broken out in certain of the afflicted countries so the problem will be in full view. The Time of Famines will have begun.

(*c*) The stricken peoples will not be able to pay for all their needed food imports. Therefore, the hunger in these regions can be alleviated only through the charity of other nations.

(*d*) Only bulk food can alleviate this hunger, which means grain. Yet the only grain available in sufficient quantity is wheat, except insofar as corn is sent to certain parts of Latin America and

Africa. Only four countries produce enough wheat to play a major role in the Time of Famines, countries I term "The Granary."

(*e*) However, three of these countries, Canada, Australia and Argentina, have in the past given only small amounts of food as charity to the hungry nations, and it is unlikely they will do more in the future. They will sell their stocks on the international market to anyone with cash in hand. Whatever these three countries may give to the needy will be only a token gesture.

(*f*) This leaves the United States as the sole hope of the hungry nations.

(*g*) Yet the United States, even if it fully cultivates all its land, even if it opens every spigot of charity, will not have enough wheat and other foodstuffs to keep alive all the starving.

THEREFORE, the United States must decide to which countries it will send food, to which countries it will not.

## *The Thesis of "Triage"*

"Triage" is a term used in military medicine. It is defined as the assigning of priority of treatment to the wounded brought to a battlefield hospital in a time of mass casualties and limited medical facilities. The wounded are divided on the basis of three classifications:

(*1*) Those so seriously wounded they cannot survive regardless of the treatment given them; call these the "can't-be-saved."

(*2*) Those who can survive without treatment regardless of the pain they may be suffering; call these the "walking wounded."

(*3*) Those who can be saved by immediate medical care.

The practice of triage is put into effect when the flow of wounded fills the tents of the battlefield hospitals and when it becomes impossible for the available medical staff to give even rudimentary care to all. Furthermore, the number allowed to be sorted into the third group for immediate treatment must be limited by the number of doctors available. The marginal cases must then also be selected out into the other two groups.

It is a terrible chore for the doctors to classify the helpless wounded in this fashion, but it is the only way to save the maximum number of lives. To spend time with the less seriously wounded or with the dying would mean that many of those who might have lived will die. It would be a misuse of the available medical help.

Call triage cold-blooded, but it is derived from the hard experience of medical humaneness during a crisis. In fact, if there is time before the battle starts, the medical staff prepares in advance the facilities to sort out these three groups.

## Triage Applied to the Time of Famines

President Johnson has proposed "that the United States lead the world in a war against hunger." [1] On the battlefields of this forthcoming war the practice of triage will be vital because choices must be made as to which wounded countries will receive our food.

The leadership in Washington comprises the medical staff. The stricken ones in need of medical attention (American food aid) are the hungry nations. To provide maximum effective treatment the medical staff must divide them into the three classifications of triage:

(1) Nations in which the population growth trend has already passed the agricultural potential. This combined with inadequate leadership and other divisive factors make catastrophic disasters inevitable. These nations form the "can't-be-saved" group. To send food to them is to throw sand in the ocean.

(2) Nations which have the necessary agricultural resources and/or foreign exchange for the purchase of food from abroad and which therefore will be able to cope with their population growth. They will be only moderately affected by the shortage of food. They are the "walking wounded" and do not require *food* aid in order to survive.

(3) Nations in which the imbalance between food and population is great but the *degree* of the imbalance is manageable. Rather, it is manageable in the sense that it can give enough time to allow the local officials to initiate effective birth control practices and to carry forward agricultural research and other forms of

development. These countries will have a chance to come through their crises provided careful medical treatment is given, that is, receipt of enough American food and also of other types of assistance.

The stocks of American food will be limited. Therefore, the extent of aid to the nations in the third group must be limited proportionately.

Call it a sieve. Adjust the size of the openings to the amount of food available to be shipped. The smaller the openings (of food), the fewer can be treated.

Unfortunately, it is not that simple. The size of a nation can itself be the determining factor against it or for it. If the available food is sent to the few big, politically important nations, then nothing will be left over for the smaller ones. Or vice versa. Thus, strictly on the basis of size and without regard to any other factors the decision might be to send food to:

Brazil but not to Central America
Central America but not Brazil
Nigeria but not the rest of West Africa
India but not Africa and Latin America

Decisions that take into account all the assorted, highly complex factors affecting differently each nation cannot be made within a vacuum. Political, economic and psychological factors must be considered. This calls for the careful analysis by experts studying the actual food capacity of the United States as set against the food needs and *survival capabilities* of the individual nations.

One delusion must be fought. Because each of these nations is hungry it is easy to jump to the conclusion that all internal problems can be solved by sending in enough food. Unfortunately, the affected nations have an assortment of wounds from an assortment of causes in addition to the food shortage. Ceylon has its language division. Sudan has its racial conflict. Bolivia has its class schism. Many have stifling corruption and graft.

In certain cases no amount of food can prevent political and social upheavals and continued, steady degeneration. Food sent to these will by itself not heal the wounds, wounds already festered.

Nor can the national interests of the United States be excluded, whether political, military or economic. American officials when applying triage decisions and shipping out *American* food are surely justified in thinking beyond only the food requirements of the individual hungry nations. They are justified, it seems to me, to consider whether the survival of a specific nation will:

(*a*) help maintain the economic viability and relative prosperity of the United States during the Time of Famines.

(*b*) help maintain the economic stability of the world as a whole.

(*c*) help create a "better" world after the troubles of the Time of Famines have ended.

No nation lives on an island all alone. Each is a part of the whole. Thus, if two nations are equal in their need for American food to increase their chances for eventual self-sufficiency but there is not enough food to send to both, then, assuredly, the one must be chosen which is better able to contribute to the foregoing three goals.

And when overall demand for food in the hungry world catches up with the American capacity to produce food (to repeat from Chapter 5: the Department of Agriculture officially forecasts this will be by 1984 and I maintain it will occur by 1975), then America's own consumption of food will have to be curtailed or altered in order to maintain the same level of food aid. For instance, curtailment of meat. Every pound of grain-fed meat that a person eats takes four to twelve pounds of feed grain. "How much grain-fed meat will the heavy meat eaters in the United States and Europe be willing to forgo in order to feed hungry people thousands of miles away?" [2]

Now is the time to recognize the implications of this. For when such shortages and/or high prices do force the American public to change their diet, it is certain that our citizens will become dead serious about this food, food which they will forgo in order to feed distant foreigners. When this happens, I take for granted that American public opinion will demand that this food be distributed in a manner which will give them their "money's worth." But unless we begin *now* to concentrate our food aid on those who can be saved during the Time of Famines, our future efforts may be ineffective. By the next decade today's savable nations may have passed beyond the point of help.

What will Americans, ten years from now, consider to be their "money's worth"? What will be a legitimate return on the food they are sending to others?

The ultimate answer, I am sure, will be stated in terms of American economic and political aims. Some can criticize this as selfish, as unhumanitarian and as unchristian. Yet the continued stability and relative prosperity of the United States during the coming decades are, surely, the single most important guarantee to insure:

— *that the world as a whole, and especially the selected hungry nations themselves, will survive the Time of Famines without sinking into chaos, and*

— *that the world will evolve into that "better" life which we hope will come to all peoples afterwards; a "better" life (both spiritual and material) is difficult to visualize as coming to fruition without the support of American capital goods which today nearly equal all those possessed by the rest of mankind.*

Therefore, I emphasize the following pertinent aspects which American officials must consider when they make their decisions as to which countries will receive our food:

(1) *Ignore the prospect that if food is withheld from a country it will "go communist."*

If a nation needs food aid to survive, then its political stability does, to a degree, depend upon that food. Like Samson's hair, when the food aid is cut off weakness will result. Assuming that the Cold War with Russia and/or China continues throughout the 1970's at its present heat (and that can be only an assumption), it is hard to see any one of these hungry nations being so vital to the United States that disaster would overwhelm our interests if it does, in fact, "go communist."

Cuba, for instance, has been a worrisome irritant to us, but not a disaster. One constantly hears the threat that India will "go communist" unless we send in ever larger amounts of food; maybe so, but a nation in the chaos of famine poses no threat of disaster to us. In any event, the drag of such deficient countries on the already weakened economies and food stocks of either Russia or China might even, in the end, be a benefit to us. One can develop a case that Cuba has been a debit, on balance, to Russia, not an asset whether economically or in international diplomacy.

(2) *Ignore the short-range political changes in these countries.*

My own guess is that the single greatest weakness of Washington in its conduct of foreign affairs since the last war has been its pusillanimous dashing to and fro, like a mouse in a cage, whenever a government is overthrown by revolution, by assassination or by correct election. Aid is rushed in or pulled out. Diplomatic recognition is quickly given on a silver platter or fitfully held back. Perhaps this is a part of the United States' becoming accustomed to its new role as the dominant world power. Whatever the reason, this has been a major cause in preventing stable foreign policies with a single nation or with a continent. During the Time of Famines revolution and turmoil will be the order of the day in most of the affected countries. To help pull a nation through the Time of Famines Washington itself must remain stable in its policies toward that nation.

(3) *Take into consideration the quality of local leadership.*

In an earlier chapter I posed the question, "In times of stress do people retrogress?" In applying the thesis of triage, that is, in selecting one country but not another to receive American food (and other forms of technical assistance), the quality of a nation's leadership must be taken into account. Without effective leaders the populace will indeed retrogress. Thus, whenever the rare quality of imaginative leadership is found, then surely it is the duty of outsiders, such as the American government, the international organizations and others, to give support in whatever manner can be extended. This support can be in the form of trade benefits or military assistance or whatever. And food — unless the nation is hopelessly in the "can't-be-saved" category or, hopefully, in the "walking wounded."

(4) *Give maximum* NON-FOOD *aid to those nations where we wish short-range political advantages.*

If we do not have enough food to supply a nation or if we have already decided it is a "walking wounded" case, then we still will have at hand the full range of our non-food resources and technical assistance with which to help it. If administered wisely this often ought to be enough to help maintain those leaders and governments whom we wish to stay in power. For instance, we have the large funds of local currencies from the "sale" of our P.L. 480 food and other supplies, i.e., the "funny money."

(5) *Favor nations which have raw materials required by the American and the world economy.*

Some countries, depending on how the Lord scattered, or failed to scatter, His largesse, produce agricultural and mineral materials which have a strategic value in today's industrial economy, while other countries do not. If a choice must be made between two equally deserving hungry nations then, certainly, the importance of keeping production lines open for a key product must be the deciding factor.

(6) *Favor nations which have military value to the United States.*

"Strategic military value" is an elusive and transitory factor amid the kaleidoscope shiftings of international politics. But it cannot be ignored by the decision-makers.

## Examples of How to Apply Triage

The clearest way to understand a theory is, of course, to apply it to specific examples. So now I present certain nations most of whom, I am sure, will make strident calls during the coming decade for American food and assistance above the levels they may already be receiving.

To bring home the painful responsibility of the official when he must himself sign the paper that will give one applicant nation priority over another, I provide a blank space where the reader can insert his own considered view of what the decision should be.

Afterwards, I give my own opinion and I recognize that my presentation of each "case" is colored by that opinion. Nevertheless, the adverse facts I state must be faced up to by the American official judging the case; and the local officials anxious to present only their country's good points must refute these same adverse facts.

## Haiti

Its population long ago exploded beyond the level of what the nation's resources can provide for a viable economy. There is nothing whatever in sight that can lift up the nation, that can alter the course of anarchy already in force for a century. At one time Haiti was one of the most agriculturally productive regions in the world, but now its fecundity has outstripped the country's resources (432 persons per square mile).[3] Now it is too late for an energetic, nationwide birth control program. (The nation is 90 per cent illiterate and has only one doctor for each 11,000 persons).[4] It is too late for intensive agricultural research efforts. The people are sunk in ignorance and indifference, and the government is entrapped in the tradition of violence.

Can't-be-saved ☐
Walking Wounded ☐
Should Receive Food ☐

## Egypt

Its population will double in twenty-three years.[5] A birth control program is being organized, but in no sense is it an all-out effort. Agricultural research and food production are static. All faith is placed in the Aswan Dam, but the production from the new land thereby opened up will be absorbed by the population born during the ten-year construction period of the dam. The area of agricultural land per Egyptian is one-fifth that for each Haitian. Meanwhile, Egypt continues to put almost no effort or money into modernizing its agriculture.[6]

Currently, Egypt has a stable government, but it is anybody's guess what conditions will prevail when Nasser is gone. Certainly, there is no tradition within the people of being able to govern themselves and to solve their own problems — and the blame cannot be laid on the Turkish and British colonialisms.

Today, the latest contract (1966) for P.L. 480 food to Egypt stipulates shipment of 538,000 metric tons over a six-month period.[7] Egypt has been the third largest recipient of American food, loans and grants. The value of this food is, in fact, almost double what Russia has contributed to the Aswan Dam.[8] Egyptian leaders give great publicity to the Russian gift but press the lid on publicity about the food from the United States.

Although Egypt has been, to repeat, the third largest recipient of our food program, Nasser consistently, year after year, does all in his power to abort American policies in the Middle East, the Congo and elsewhere through deliberate acts of subversive plots, alleged attempted assassinations of neighboring leaders friendly to the United States and open, active support of anti-American regimes throughout the area.

In the interplay of international politics there is, of course, the importance of assuring that the Suez Canal is kept open to world shipping. In fact, this seems to be about the only specific point of interest that the United States has within Egypt. If worst comes to worst (that most dire of vague phrases) the Canal could be kept open to world shipping by militarily occupying the canal strip and cordoning it off from the rest of Egypt. In today's political context such action would rightly be considered an example of fantasy; in tomorrow's chaos of the Time of Famines it could be another matter.

The Egyptian problem is, probably, within the capabilities of United States resources. To control a problem of this size, however, would mean to curtail or cancel food shipments to other needy nations. The Egyptians themselves, if current trends remain, will never in the foreseeable future be able to feed themselves or to generate enough foreign exchange with which to buy the food.

|  |  |
|---|---|
| Can't-be-saved | ☐ |
| Walking Wounded | ☐ |
| Should Receive Food | ☐ |

### The Gambia

Perhaps no country has such artificial boundaries as The Gambia, either economically or politically. Yet, oddly enough, the population (300,000) and the national economy seem to be in balance with their sliver of land, twenty miles wide and three hundred miles long. It has no more agricultural land per person than does Haiti, but all the land borders on a navigable river.

A few years ago I traveled in a small boat the length of the Gambia River. My chief impression was of the relaxed, full life of the people within the traditions of their culture. Outsiders and also the elite of the capital city can argue that progress in the country is hopeless until those same traditions are thrown aside and replaced with the "modern" life. My only answer is that the Gambians probably will be glad they have not yet progressed into the "modern" life when they see the crises and turmoil of those countries around them which attempted development beyond the base of their resources. The chief problem of The Gambia now is to hold back its population increase and to hold back its capital, Bathurst, to its present size — without it exploding into the usual city slum so typical of other African capitals and thereby overpowering the government with city problems.

With only one doctor for every 16,000 persons and a population 80 per cent illiterate,[9] The Gambia will need foreign aid and technical assistance, but should this include an allotment of American food, even the small amount needed for this small nation?

|  |  |
|---|---|
| Can't-be-saved | ☐ |
| Walking Wounded | ☐ |
| Should Receive Food | ☐ |

*Tunisia*

A few years ago AID retreated from its former policy of worldwide, try-to-save-everybody programs and concentrated its major efforts on a half-dozen carefully selected nations (a clean-cut example that it is indeed possible for Washington to choose certain countries for help and to ignore others, which is essentially this thesis of triage I am discussing).

One of the chosen nations of AID has been Tunisia. Just before this intensified program began I traveled in native buses the length of the country. I was depressed by the low quality of the farmland and the backwardness of the rural areas. Yet today, due not only to the concentration of American help but even more to the intelligent supervision of the Tunisian leadership, steady economic and social progress is under way. Although the population will double in thirty-three years[10] and the agricultural output per capita has decreased during the period 1948-1963,[11] Tunisia has three acres of agricultural land per person,[12] a high figure in today's world. Also it has agricultural phosphate deposits. Thus, it does have an agricultural potential. Approximately $20 million in food from the United States was programmed to Tunisia for 1965, the last year published.[13] An official birth control program is under way after a preliminary two-year experimental project,[14] and recent agricultural progress has been encouraging.

In the hope that extra food supplies will keep this progress in motion and will help maintain a stable government after Bourguiba is gone, should the United States continue to send food stocks to Tunisia (where American political and economic interests are minor) rather than to another country?

Can't-be-saved ☐
Walking Wounded ☐
Should Receive Food ☐

### Libya

Probably, no area has received so much aid attention as Libya, not only from the United States but also from Great Britain and others. The succession of foreign aid and technical assistance teams and advisers that have gone to Libya since the war form a case study of this whole subject. In varying degrees this help did have an effect, but seldom beyond the propping up stage. It did not result in creating the forces which would develop the nation, nor was this ever even in prospect. The resources of the country were then too paltry, the population increases too steady.

Then, glory be, oil spouted forth and now the nation has an income that ought to be able to cover its needs.

I was in and out of Libya a few times before the oil was discovered and when it was a most backward country. What it is like now with all the excitement the oil has engendered I can only dimly visualize. Yet now the oil is gushing out in sufficient quantity to support the country if the leadership and the public keep their "rising expectations" down to the level for which the oil can pay — but, on the contrary, the "rising expectations" are spiraling upward like an unchecked hot air balloon.

The population is spiraling upward just as fast. So far, there is no birth control program and its population growth is the second highest in all Africa.[15] The United States has not sent food to Libya for several years and now, fortunately, the resources are at hand, namely the oil, with which Libya can buy abroad the food it needs.

Yet with a doubled population within nineteen years[16] one foresees the demand for Food for Freedom supplies that probably will come from Libya. When it does, should the answer be "yes"?

Can't-be-saved ☐
Walking Wounded ☐
Should Receive Food ☐

*India*

India is the example that cuts across all the political and economic guide rules I have been using for the other nations. Also, more than in any other country, if the United States should today cut off its food aid, or even curtail it, immediate turmoil and possible catastrophe would result.

Today India absorbs like a blotter 25 per cent of the entire American wheat crop. Nearly all of this is sent as P.L. 480 food.

No matter how one may adjust present statistics and allow for future increases in the American wheat crop, for future shipments of rice and corn to India and for a possible increase of India's own production of grains, today's trends show it will be beyond the resources of the United States to keep famine out of India during the 1970's. Indian agriculture is too antiquated. Its present government is too inefficient to inaugurate long-range agricultural development programs. Its population tidal wave is too overwhelming, more than 11,500,000 are added each year to the current half-billion population.[17]

Thus far, the Indian leadership, beginning with Nehru, appears to have botched just about every effort at progress in local food development and population control that has been offered to it.

"As one Indian farmer puts it, 'The bureaucrats aren't hungry, so they just won't get excited.' " [18]

Of all the national leaderships the Indian comes close to being the most childish and inefficient and perversely determined to cut the country's economic throat. But, except for a degree of graft, it is not an evil leadership like those of some other nations. It is not looting the country or threatening rapine on its neighbors. It is just childish. There is little reason to believe that future American help will result in a more responsible Indian leadership than our past help has effected.

So the famines will come. Riding alongside will surely be riots and other civil tensions which the central government will be too weak to control.

Throughout the past decade the American shipments of food to India have escalated planlessly each year. We have committed our resources to the country's short-term emergencies, *not* to long-range development. Step by step we have so added to our responsibility that now Washington cannot afford, it fears, to let that country sink. To save the "investment" of $6.5 billion[19] we have already put into India, to save the nation from breaking up into civil disorder, to save it from "going communist," we are rushing in more and more food. We have drifted along until now it is too late to make decisions on the basis of what is the best use of our food capacity for filling worldwide needs. India is moving quickly toward taking so much of our available food that, if continued, our food aid to other countries must soon be slashed.

Although I emphasize the planlessness it is important to repeat that a planned disposal of our surpluses was never the intent of the P.L. 480 law, nor has it been a governing instruction for the officials of this program. They were charged with the quite different task of just getting rid of the food. The result in India, therefore, is that our officials were not required to sit back and ask, "Do we have enough food to save India? Could all the world save India? Is India worth this food if other countries are to be lost?" Under triage such decisions would have to be made.

In retrospect it is hard to see any positive, direct advantage the United States has received from its $6.5 billion of aid to India, other than the negative one of, so far, bolstering a sort of stable nation. Although the vituperative blasts against all things American that the Indian representative used to shout in the United Nations are now muted, the present government continues to work actively against many American policies in the assorted chancelleries of the world. Yet this has done little harm, one way or another, to the United States.

If we cut off the food to India we are not losing a reliable friend. Nor do we gain an enemy able to do us serious hurt.

On the other hand, we do condemn a segment of the human race to disastrous suffering, people who, in the end, may be as worthy to receive our limited food aid as other, perhaps equally neuter, nations.

Can't-be-saved ☐
Walking Wounded ☐
Should Receive Food ☐

## Pakistan

Throughout this book I have sort of sidestepped Pakistan, although several times I could have used it as an illustration, sometimes favorable to it, sometimes not.

On the surface it suffers from the same troubles, the same malaise, as the rest of the undeveloped world. It is indeed a candidate for mass starvation in the 1970's. Its population of 115,000,000 — which will double in twenty-five years[20] — makes effective aid from the United States a stupendous job and one which must perforce divert our energies and resources away from many smaller nations.

Birth control programs are not yet intensive, but they have had a firm background in the efforts since 1953 of the Family Planning Association of Pakistan to popularize family planning. Also, since 1958 they have had the strong support of President Ayub Khan who has made them a part of the national development plan and even included his advocacy in his election platform manifesto.[21] This fifteen-year history, combined with Ayub's type of government, may indeed have an effect on the birth rate within the next couple of decades.

Most important of all, Pakistan has a unique asset now working for it: it is one undeveloped country whose top leadership seems to have faced up to the problem of feeding the exploding population. So far, apparently, the effort is concentrated primarily on expanding the wheat production of West Pakistan, thus for the most part letting the rice of East Pakistan and other types of crops remain in their time-worn ruts. Nevertheless, it is so unusual for the key men in an undeveloped country to give full support to even one part of the agriculture that Pakistan is today special. And, of course, success with the wheat crop may spill over and favorably affect the rest of the agriculture.

The interest in wheat was generated by the availability of the same Dr. Norman Borlaug whom I mentioned in Chapter 3 in connection with his successful development of new wheats in Mexico. These are of a dwarf variety designed especially for the application of fertilizer; they do not fall over and lodge even when too much fertilizer is put on. Since parts of West Pakistan have climates similar to those of Mexico (and the local populace is accustomed to eating this type of wheat), the introduction of the new Mexican wheats was, technologically, relatively easy.

After a preliminary four years of research in Pakistan, 350 tons of Mexican seed were imported in 1965. From this initial amount enough seed will have been produced by the end of 1967 so that a target of 6 million acres (half of Pakistan's wheat acreage) is set to be planted with the new wheats in the fall of 1967.[22] And a major portion of this acreage can be irrigated the same as in Mexico.

Borlaug and his Mexican colleagues have now trained a staff of Pakistani researchers. This, coupled with the backing of the Rockefeller and Ford Foundations and the support of President Ayub, can make an effective task force. Officials who were fearful, suspicious, or jealous of the new men and their ideas, a situation well known in Washington and all other bureaucracies, have been converted or transferred. Other roadblocks will continue to be laid down by minor bureaucrats and local scientists, but the overall progress is assured.

The technicians in charge say that *if* they and Pakistan's 4,000-man agricultural extension service can plant 30,000 to 40,000 demonstration plots (so the local farmers can see the value of the new wheats when fertilized) and *if* adequate fertilizer is available, *then*

Pakistan can be self-sufficient in this vital grain in 1968 or 1969. They even anticipate Pakistan exporting wheat in 1970! [23]

These are formidable "ifs" to overcome, but the record so far would seem to warrant the high hopes.

Nevertheless, despite the optimism of everyone connected with this program, can even maximum success meet the food demands of an additional 115,000,000 persons rolling in on the tide of the next twenty-five years? This wheat may in time be the salvation of West Pakistan, but it is doubtful that East Pakistan will receive similar hope until its own agriculture is accelerated. In fact, the true moment of crisis will come for Pakistan when the one half of the nation retains hope of adequate food but the other half sinks without hope into famine. It is hard to see how West Pakistan, even with the most sincere sacrificing of its own food stocks, can itself transport enough wheat to East Pakistan to save that region, a thousand miles away across a hostile, equally hungry India or three times as far by sea.

Through the years Pakistan has been, next to India, the largest recipient of American aid. Yet the leaders of all parties blithely ignore this in their active opposition to most American international policies and they ignore the omens that their nation must continue to be dependent on this aid.

Politically and militarily Pakistan has value to the United States because of accumulated activities and installations resulting from CENTO and SEATO. Actually, however, it is about as queasy an ally as France is to NATO.

If the United States continues to send P.L. 480 food to this elephant-sized, apathetic "ally," it may be possible to keep East Pakistan quiescent for a decade or so and thus, perhaps, give West Pakistan enough time to press forward birth control and to increase food production in order to prevent at least that part of the nation from foundering. As for East Pakistan it must surely sink into famine unless drastic and comprehensive programs for agriculture are immediately started; this the national leadership, the majority of whose background is in the West, seems unable to initiate.

Although one can say that the saving of a half a loaf, namely West Pakistan, is better than giving up the entire loaf, nevertheless the size of American food shipments, directed to the nation as a whole, would probably have to remain at the present gigantic scale.

Can't-be-saved            ☐
Walking Wounded           ☐
Should Receive Food       ☐

My own opinion as to the triage classification of these sample nations is:

| | |
|---|---|
| Haiti | Can't-be-saved |
| Egypt | Can't-be-saved |
| The Gambia | Walking Wounded |
| Tunisia | Should Receive Food |
| Libya | Walking Wounded |
| India | Can't-be-saved |
| Pakistan | Should Receive Food |

These examples seem to me to adhere closely to the basic triage divisions for the use of American *food* up to and during the Time of Famines. Those that I say should receive our shipments have within the foreseeable future a valid chance to obtain self-sufficiency in food or, at least, to achieve an important improvement in self-sufficiency. This will be due primarily to their own efforts and resources. They are far enough along with their population control and agricultural research and development programs to hope that they eventually will hold their own. Furthermore, political factors are adequately stabilized to give these programs a chance for success.

But what about the countries which are doing little or nothing to overcome their population growth and static agriculture and yet which are, for some specific reason, vital to the economy of the United States and the rest of the world? I call these "The Exceptions." For example:

*Panama*

Not only does the United States have a vital interest that the Panama Canal be kept open, but so has the rest of the world. Unlike the Suez Canal, it cannot be isolated from the rest of the country.

Panama's population explosion (one of the world's highest) versus its static agriculture is as serious as that in any Latin American country. This adverse ratio must be resolved before the country can ever achieve tranquillity. Yet so far little is being done. The country is continuing to drift passively along the brink of chaos. The not-so-latent anti-American feeling is all-pervasive. Even though the chief cause of this, the once abrasive American staff of the Panama Canal Company, is now less conspicuous, it is doubtful that the feeling against the United States will decrease materially.

Meantime, the cost and logistics of sending food to this miniature nation (1,200,000 population)[24] is minimal and the amount of food required in the decades ahead will not appreciably affect other food aid programs qualifying under triage. Therefore, put Panama on the dole and consider it a form of subsidy for the Canal.

### Bolivia

If a nation is fortunate to possess a resource vital to the world's needs, that nation often can market it at a high enough price to buy with the proceeds the amount of food it needs. There are countries, however, where the value of the product, although vital, is not enough to do this.

Venezuela probably throughout this century ought to be able to buy the food it needs from its oil receipts. On the other hand, the world demand for the equally vital tin has failed to keep Bolivia solvent. If, as the Time of Famines approaches, civil unrest cuts off the tin from export to the outside world, should the United States send in the large amount of food necessary to keep the country stable and the flow of tin open?

The population of Bolivia is 3,700,000 but fortunately it is growing at a rate (1.4 per cent per year)[25] even lower than that of the United States. The agriculture of the *altiplano* (where the population is centered) is surely among the most difficult and unrewarding in the world; it is hard to see how even unlimited capital or a large research program, if one is ever started, could produce adequate results there. This puts the future hope of the country in the now sparsely inhabited tropical areas; here, as in the rest of the tropical world, the research must start from scratch in order to bring forth, some day, successful new techniques which, years later, can be put into operation in the area.

In the meantime, the social unrest and the revolutions that have spasmodically disrupted the country for a generation will undoubtedly continue. It is easy to understand and sympathize with the causes of the social tensions, but it is hard to predict how the country can ever get on its feet economically, even with maximum income from tin, until the tropical areas become farmable.

Thus, American food support would be needed far into the future. It would be an open-end obligation once the responsibility is accepted. Yet I am told by officials that the uninterrupted export of the tin is a strategic necessity. Accordingly, I would place this case among the exceptions to receive American food.

### The Philippines

Here the population is 32,000,000,[26] thus definitely removing it from the "small nation" class. Worse, birth control programs remain in the some-day-in-the-future stage.

When I was traveling in Mindanao a Filipino lumberman summed up his country: "From the Spanish we became experts in dirty government; from the Chinese we became experts in dirty business; from the Americans we became experts in dirty graft." Which is partly true and partly passing the buck. Certainly, few peoples so irritate and frustrate the outsiders who live there or try to deal with them. Yet few people are so lively and outgoing. The country is Asia's freest democracy. Seventy-five per cent of the population is literate.[27] When I was stationed at the embassy in Manila my personal impression was that whatever the Japanese can do the Filipinos could do just as well — if they would only calm down and concentrate on the job at hand.

On the credit side, the agricultural university, one of the few in the tropical world, is a good one and it is growing better. Henry Heald, recently retired president of the Ford Foundation, predicts that the International Rice Research Institute, located at the university, "is going to make a greater contribution to feeding Southeast Asia in the next 10 years than all the food the U.S. can ship over there or all the aid the U.S. government can provide."[28]

On the debit side, the nation's agriculture is so archaic that its yields of rice per acre are among the lowest in the world. The per capita annual income is $140 (one of the highest in the undeveloped countries) but the figure is lopsided because 70 per cent of the population is engaged in subsistence farming.[29] Housing for the average Filipino is deplorable, communications poor. Graft is notorious. Politics is usually one of groupings around demagogic leaders — although the present administration of Ferdinand Marcos is far above the caliber of its predecessor and is also combatting the traditional graft.

The rate of population explosion here is near the top, but in this country where the Catholic church is so dominant in the halls of government, birth control programs are not even considered. The population will double in twenty-two years.[30] Thus, no matter how miraculously the new research programs may improve agriculture the gains will be washed out by this tidal wave of new births.

In the argument whether it should or should not receive American food the Philippines would seem to have, on balance, not much more in their favor than their neighbors in Asia — except for one factor. The Filipinos do retain a pro-American attitude that, on the whole, still permeates most levels of the national society. The strength of this attitude is almost unique throughout the undeveloped world. True, this pro-Americanism is stormed-tossed by adverse winds from many sources, including huffs and puffs from various American political and military officials. Yet the pro-Americanism remains an important force which should, when possible, be nurtured.

American food can help this nurturing.

Therefore, I would place the Philippines among the exceptions to receive American food — at least until its uncontrolled population explosion gets completely out of hand or until it becomes impossible to send supplies there without endangering our shipments to those other nations which have more forcefully resolved their population problems.

Here is the total list of 111 countries and dependencies which in 1965 received food from the United States under P.L. 480.[31] Where within the framework of triage does each belong?

| | | | |
|---|---|---|---|
| Aden | Egypt | Lebanon | St. Vincent |
| Afghanistan | El Salvador | Libya | Senegal |
| Algeria | Ethiopia | Macao | Seychelles |
| Antigua | Fiji | Malagasy Rep. | Sierra Leone |
| Basutoland | France | Malawi | Singapore |
| Bolivia | Gabon | Malaysia | Somalia |
| Brazil | Gambia | Mali | Spain |
| British Guiana | Gaza | Malta | Sudan |
| British Honduras | Ghana | Martinique | Surinam |
| British Solomon | Greece | Mauritania | Swaziland |
| Islands | Grenada | Mauritius | Syria |
| Burma | Guadeloupe | Mexico | Tanzania |
| Burundi | Guatemala | Montserrat | Thailand |
| Cambodia | Guinea | Morocco | Togo |
| Cameroons | Haiti | Nicaragua | Tongo Islands |
| Central African | Honduras | Nigeria | Trieste |
| Republic | Hong Kong | Okinawa | Trinidad and |
| Ceylon | India | Pakistan | Tobago |
| Chad | Indonesia | Panama | Tunisia |
| Chile | Iran | Paraguay | Turkey |
| China (Taiwan) | Iraq | Peru | Turks and Caicos |
| Colombia | Israel | Philippine | Islands |
| Congo | Italy | Islands | Uganda |
| Costa Rica | Ivory Coast | Poland | Upper Volta |
| Cyprus | Jamaica | Portugal | Uruguay |
| Dahomey | Jordan | Rwanda | Venezuela |
| Dominica | Kenya | St. Helena | Vietnam |
| Dominican Rep. | Korea | St. Kitts | Yeman |
| Ecuador | Laos | St. Lucia | Yugoslavia |

## In the End the Responsibility Lies with America's Officials

The weakness of triage lies in its implementation by a demo-cratic government like that of the United States. The democratic process does not lend itself to thinking through coldly and logically a complex problem such as American food versus the world's hun-gry, trying to formulate a practical program before the crisis strikes and then sticking with it through several administrations. The strength of triage is that it satisfies what I assume will be the demands of:

(*a*) *the humanitarians:* to save the maximum number of lives during the Time of Famines.
(*b*) *the patriots:* to safeguard the economic stability of the United States.
(*c*) *the diplomats:* to safeguard the political, economic and strategic interests of the United States on all continents.
(*d*) *the realists:* to keep our goals within the limits of our resources.

Equally important, triage fits existing legislation. It gives a jumping-off point for the leaders in Washington to begin their analysis of what our government will do with our foodstuffs that soon will be forthcoming from the land under the new Food for Peace concept of "turning the farmers loose." Today's India has alerted one and all to the magnitude of the problem created by the population explosion in the face of static agriculture.

Washington may dally and shuffle and procrastinate, but the Moment of Truth will come the morning when the President must make a choice whether to save India or to save Latin America, when he must sign a piece of paper to send available food to one of two neighboring countries but not to the other, though both are equally friendly to the United States, both equally worthy of help.

Let us hope that before this Moment of Truth arrives there has been wide discussion of this problem in the press, in church councils, in Congress and in the departments of the government. The many-faceted problems of the choices of triage, the most far-reaching problem of the coming generation, cannot be resolved on the spur of the hour or, worse, on a fluctuating day-to-day, crisis-to-crisis basis.

This is so because during this discussion in the open forum of a democracy, the following compromises must be reached:

(*a*) The humanitarians must come to realize it will be impossible to save everyone, that choices must be made, that logical, thought-out choices are themselves the essence of humanitarianism.

(b) The patriots must come to realize that the economic stability of the United States is weakened, not strengthened, by a policy of isolationism.

(c) The diplomats must come to realize that although the Time of Famines will last for several decades it will indeed end some day; and when it does end then the interests of the United States will be served best by independent friends, not subordinate retainers.

(d) The realists must accept the policy of utilizing our resources to the maximum, not the minimum, in behalf of the hope, the quite practical hope, of a "better" world when the Time of Famines gives way to the Next Age.

Finally, everyone — the Bolivians, the Indians, the Gambians, the Zambians, the Trinidadians and, most of all, the Americans — must realize that when a 10,000-ton freighter loaded to the scuppers with Food for Peace wheat sails out of New York or Baltimore or Seattle or Buffalo or Houston a specific component of American wealth is shipped out, wealth in the form of 200 tons of nitrogen, 41 tons of phosphorus and 50 tons of potassium.[32] Multiply these figures by the approximately 14,600 freighter loads shipped out from 1954 to July 1965 and one sees that the portion of our soil's fertility thus lost forever is a significant part of our national resources, resources which we are denying to our children and grandchildren.

Also carried within the freighter is American wealth in the form of the farmers' labor, the depreciation of the tractors, the consumption of the diesel fuel, the use of the transportation system which moved the wheat to the ports and the labor that loaded the ships. The shiploads of food (and currently we are rushing to India 1,000,000 tons a month, or three to four ships *each day*) are not a gift which "has cost nobody nothing." They are as real as the gold in Fort Knox.

When we pour out this wealth we ought to get something in return for it. Let us make certain that what we get from our future shipments is a "better" world for our children. They are the ones who will suffer if we fail to obtain a fair return on this forfeiture of national resources.

Triage would seem to be the most clean-cut method of meeting the crisis. Waste not the food on the "can't-be-saved" and the "walking wounded." Send it to those nations which, having it, can buttress their own resources, their own efforts, and win the fight through to survival.

# 10

## The Time of Famines Can Be the Catalyst for a Period of American Greatness

As is the way with authors, I submitted the manuscript of this book for comment to friends who are experts in various of the fields touching this subject, including officials from some of the countries discussed here so adversely.

It was disheartening to note that no matter what other agreements or disagreements they offered and no matter how diverse their assorted backgrounds were, each one still believed that "something will turn up" to deflect the Time of Famines. That "something," however, was never in their own field of expertise; always each advocated "solutions" in other areas.

Thus, I here suggest it would be well for the reader to review Chapter 3 which lists these "somethings." And I emphasize again that synthetic foods will not turn aside man's hunger a decade from now, nor fish from the sea, nor irrigation with water from desalinization, nor culture by hydroponics, nor fertilizer, nor the cultivation of new land in the "vast, untapped" jungles or arid wastelands, nor land reforms, nor socialistic controls, nor capitalistic initiatives. Nor will research produce in time new seeds, new techniques, new plants for the farmers to sow and reap.

All of these combined can be the salvation of the twenty-first century. Any one of these could achieve a sudden leap forward in progress before the end of this century. Yet none, alone or in combination with each other, will have major effect on the food crises of the 1970's.

"Something" will *not* turn up.

Regarding those who read the manuscript I must, to be honest, admit that the reaction of some to the thesis of triage was, to quote one of the men, "complete horror." Most Americans are simply not conditioned to withholding food from the hungry. With these men it was not a matter of disagreeing with my examples of specific countries in relation to triage; they realized these were subject to individual interpretation.

Unfortunately, the fact that America's abundance is limited has itself created the problem of choosing who is to receive the food. The American people cannot slough off the responsibility of this distribution except by turning it over, for instance, to the United Nations. Such action would result in its dissipation either on an ineffectively minuscule per capita basis or to those countries doing the fastest wheeling and dealing within the U.N. corridors.

No, America's bountiful land has imposed on us a *noblesse oblige* which we must face up to.

The victory in the fight for world supremacy may not go to the one who has accomplished the most spectacular fireworks, but rather to the party which does something to alleviate the distress among peoples of the earth.[1]

I think we have a moral obligation to ourselves to make certain that our commitments do not out-pace our anticipated productivity, with the result that benevolence would bring down our own house.[2]

When you look at the historic record of the United States, the American people, once confronted with a famine, have never really debated what to do. We have just responded. It is so deeply in our nature that it seems to me that when we are confronted with millions of people dying in the streets in any country, we are going to respond to it. So isn't the real question whether we are going to wait for that catastrophe to hit, and then respond in some kind of a makeshift emergency fashion, or whether we are going to start laying careful plans now and taking some steps to prevent what we know will otherwise be a catastrophe?[3]

We in the United States are in a position of overwhelming responsibility at the present time, for in a very real sense the destiny of humanity depends upon our decisions and upon our actions. We still possess freedom, our resources, and our knowledge to stimulate the evolution of a world community within which people are well fed and within which they can lead abundant lives. Or we can refuse to take constructive action, in which case man will almost certainly start down the steep incline. . . . Never before in history has so much responsibility been inherited by a group of human beings.[4]

These quotations arrive, from different viewpoints, at the same conclusion: a crucial period in world history is at hand and the means for guiding the world through this period lie with the American people. The United States with its agricultural capacity combined with its other resources is the only nation able to give leadership for coping with the Time of Famines.

Today's international strategy of power politics is based on who has atomic weapons and who has not, plus the sophistication of how the "have" nation pushes forward its policies without making use of its ultimate persuader.

Before the end of the 1970's the interplay of power politics will be based on who is starving and who is not, who has extra food to send to others and who has not. Food will be the basis for power. Here the sophistication will lie in the need for the "food nation" to select which countries, out of the many hungry ones, will receive its limited food stocks, which countries will be left in the miseries of their starvation.

Today's Atomic Age will give way to the Age of Food. "I only wish the press of America were as interested in the power of food as they are of missiles. . . . Missiles and nuclear weapons are worthless with starving people. . . . Food is life. . . . Food is wealth. . . . Food is power, because a nation without food is powerless." [5]

During the coming Age of Food that nation which has the most food will be, if it uses that food as a source of power, the strongest nation. This will be, then, clearly an era which the United States can dominate — if the United States picks up the challenge.

Twice before, after World Wars I and II, the United States was for a moment the dominant world power. It did not use immediately that strength to further either the world's or its own long-range interests. This was due partly to our own boredom with things of war and partly to our inability to conceive of ourselves as the dominant power. Thus, each time the world drifted into a state of troubles detrimental both to itself and to the United States.

Now America, through the world's food shortage, has a third chance to take time by the forelock and soften approaching adversities. It has the chance, but will it succeed? There are, alas, many obstacles to overcome and most seem to be of a difficult psychological, rather than of an easy physical, nature.

## Obstacle No. 1: Capacity of Leadership in Washington

The United States will have the power, but the degree of its success will depend on the quality of leadership in Washington, namely, the leadership that evolves out of the moral stamina, the ability and the imagination of the American people.

"A significant percentage of our brightest and most capable young people, the ones best suited for leadership, is simply not interested [in the classic American formula of ambition and worldly success]. They don't covet the pains and rewards of responsibility." [6]

As Secretary of Health, Education and Welfare, John W. Gardner, sees it, the educative process itself is at fault: "The academic world appears to be approaching a point at which everyone will want to educate the technical expert who advises the leader, or the intellectual who stands off and criticizes the leader, but no one will want to educate the leader himself." [7]

So far, fortunately, our history seems to prove that we usually produce gifted men to cope with specific major international crises. By some alchemy of democracy the men suited to the crisis rise to meet it, regardless of how dubious their earlier backgrounds may have been. Lincoln, Hay, Stimson, the two Roosevelts, Truman, Acheson would be examples.

Nevertheless, doubt is expressed now by American intellectuals as to whether our present form of complicated elective government can produce effective leadership, leadership with the quality of greatness, during a *constant* crisis continuing decade after decade. In the prolonged military crisis of the Cold War our leadership has remained generally effective. The Time of Famines, however, will not have the stimulus of military enemies in full sight. There will be no physical danger to keep the public unified, only the spiritual/humanitarian faith that we are doing "good." Amid such vagueness the quality of American leadership may well taper off. Not only will there be the ever present pressures to use our food producing capacity for purely economic gains, but there will be the pressures of brush-fire international crises. Most of these headlines might be resolved on a short-term basis by quick shipments of food; it will require leadership of strength to hoard the foodstocks and to adhere to formulated policies, such as a Plan of Triage.

History has not been kind to democracies. They seem to fall apart if the pressure of crisis is maintained too long. However, neither is history kind to totalitarian leadership. When The Man is gone, so is stability, until a new Man arises. Meantime, all is turmoil.

Perhaps our government is already, subconsciously, evolving itself into a firmer posture of strength to meet the hard decisions of responsibility of the future. Today's executive branch is steadily becoming more powerful. Yet the nation remains a democracy. This compromise in the system of government might well be the key factor in keeping our country on an even keel through the forthcoming period of troubles.

## Obstacle No. 2: The Softening of American Society

It is misleading to take for granted that American society itself will remain unchanged in the decades ahead, that today's dynamic stability will continue. For a key question is this: Can the American people maintain the hard moral strength and the physical drive which the leadership must have supporting it in order to lead the rest of the world effectively?

It is at this point that many of America's most contemplative thinkers begin their worrying.

The forecast is that today's affluence will indeed continue for an indefinite period ahead, such as into the 1980's. This would make the period of supreme prosperity cover two generations and more. Many have doubts the American people can maintain their present dynamism that long within the framework of luxuriant living, steady incomes and meticulous attention to health and physical safety. Although there are still pockets of poverty (a most accurate phrase), they do not affect the whole. The American public as a unit will continue to live within a downy cocoon to a degree never before experienced in the world for such a long period.

In a conversation I had with Herman Kahn, Director of the Hudson Institute, he expressed the deep concern which many have pertaining to the effects of this cocoon existence. He said:

> By the late 1970's there may be no poor in the United States, not even pockets of poverty as we understand the term today. The work week could be down to 30 or 35 hours and almost everyone could be taking vacations of from one to three months. Nevertheless, industry could continue to spew out ever-increasing amounts of manufactured goods and other material goods and services. The GNP could continue to grow at a rate of about 4 per cent a year, in part because our government will understand how to deal with cyclic changes and maintenance of overall demand.
>
> But, by and large, this would not be growth derived from energetic drive, hard work and risk-taking innovations within the people, as has been the case up to now. Nor will these be as necessary. Therefore, at some point in the years ahead Americans, on balance, could cease to be an action-motivated, achievement-oriented, work-oriented people. There may also be extreme over-reactions. The current wave of beatniks are, most likely, a forerunner for a greater number of similarly disillusioned people, disillusioned and frustrated in the sense that life has no meaning, or, rather, no satisfying goals (other than an existential hedonism or a superficial mysticism) to strive for.
>
> Thus, by the 1970's the United States will have lost a great deal of its moral purpose and drive. It will not be the same country that it is today, in the same way that we are not now the same hard people who conquered the wilderness and created our present industrial and agricultural base.[8]

One often hears that Americans are rapidly abandoning the "Protestant ethic" that served as the foundation on which the nation was built and prospered. Instead, soon there will be dominant "the Grecian love of relaxation and beauty."

I am not sure just what the term "Protestant ethic" means, and my analysis of the ancient Greeks is that they hankered for the relaxed life of leisure and beauty just about like everyone else. The one Greek state of Athens that did climb up to this nice mezzanine, or at least the elite did, and that for barely two generations,

soon withered, was conquered and thereafter drifted along in political unimportance. Hence, such terms are rather misleading except
to indicate that many analytical minds today foresee a radical shift
in American attitudes within the next couple of decades.

Certainly, our American forefathers' traditional Calvinistic belief in the rewards of hard work — the Lord helps those who help
themselves, it is sinful to squander, it is righteous to save — is no
longer paramount as the nation's ideal. One can mourn its loss and
say that the fiber of the nation will now become less hardy, less self-
reliant.

One must also recognize, however, that such a sturdy creed was
necessary and suitable in the harsh days of pioneering, of beating
back the Indians, of conquering the wilderness, of surviving vicious
economic depressions. It is unrealistic to expect the same creed, the
same ideals, to control men's minds in today's luxurious prosperity.

Today the individual citizen has no dragon to fight in mortal
combat, nor lurking Indian, nor blizzards, nor locusts, nor the fearsome isolation of the remote farmhouse. Today's only physical enemies are that other automobile and the city mugger.

This is also true of the nation as a whole. As long as the Cold
War posed a dangerous, ruthless enemy ready to pounce on us,
then this served to maintain our national alertness, our own mus-
cled posture of defense. Without such an enemy beyond the gates
— and Russia does seem a much less scary opponent than a decade
ago — then there is indeed the prospect that flabbiness may replace the present American dynamism.

Ergo: How well can the American people maintain their old
strengths of character during decade after decade of rich prosperity
combined with the dominant international position our food
stocks have created? And if the American people do not maintain
their strength of purpose, what then is to become of the power for
"good" contained in its stocks of food? Will the power dribble out
like sand between the soft fingers? Is it useless to try to formulate a
Plan of Triage?

A clergyman was quoted in a magazine article:

The trouble with most of us isn't active or deliberate wickedness; it's
lethargy, absence of caring, lack of involvement in life. To keep our

bodies comfortable and well-fed and entertained seems to be all that matters. But the more successful we are at this, the more entombed the soul becomes in solid, immovable flesh. We no longer hear the distant trumpet and go toward it; we listen to the pipes of Pan and fall asleep. How can I rouse my people, make them yearn for something more than pleasant, socially acceptable ways of escaping from life? How can I make them want to thrust forward into the unknown, into the world of testing and trusting their own spirit? Oh, how I wish I knew! [9]

## Obstacle No. 3: The Temptation to Drift Back into Isolationism

By the end of the 1970's many observers anticipate that the American people will have swung full cycle into a passive isolationism, deeper than at any previous time in our history.

Isolationism will be the antithesis of a Plan of Triage, for the Plan calls for active and strong involvement in the affairs of a fair proportion of the world beyond our borders.

A review of a television documentary about the high school age group of a prosperous Middle West suburb said:

The youngsters are privileged, satisfied, content, smug. There's no adventure, rebellion, dissatisfaction in them. They think having a nice personality and good looks is more important than being a good student. They want the diploma but not the learning. They cheat to get good grades. They can identify Dick Van Dyke but not Ho Chi Minh. They are regimented and insulated by their parents against war, death and poverty. The non-college group and the intellectuals don't fit in. If the biopsy of this microcosm . . . is true of the country, then America is in grave danger of a new isolationism, one created by self-imposed blinders.[10]

With American power so preeminent, with no physical danger from any source, the Americans, these intellectual critics believe, will lose interest in foreign troubles. They might, in fact, not even recognize the power their food gives to them. More pertinent, the Americans may lose their sense of responsibility to help others, an attitude that has until now firmly reinforced legitimate American self-interest in its foreign aid projects and in the former P.L. 480 program.

It is true that the tradition of isolationism recurs periodically throughout the flow of American history. As a policy, however, it is strong only when we are not threatened from beyond our borders; isolationism seems to collapse as soon as we must face up to such threats. During the Time of Famines it is doubtful we will see any physical threat to the safety of the country.

A relapse into isolationism would affect many phases of American life, but here I am concerned only with the aspect that would influence implementation of a Plan of Triage.

In international matters we are now in the position of a poker player who has been extremely successful during a night's playing and wants to pick up his chips and go home. But the other players won't let him. We have more than 40 per cent of the world's goods for only 6 per cent of the world's population. We might like to get out of the game and just make some foreign aid gifts, altruistically, to the other players. But we can't go home. We have to stay in the game.

By the 1970's, however, this may have changed. By then Russia itself will probably have tended to isolate herself from the rest of the world, concentrating on economic growth, consumer goods, and internal problems. Today Russia has several such problems — no one really knows how serious they are — misunderstandings with foreign Communist parties and governments, serious trouble with its industry, its agriculture, and most important of all with its youth and its elites. No one knows what all this may lead to. One prospect, however, is that Russia will withdraw into itself — in part to concentrate on solving these problems. This should cut down and perhaps eliminate conflict with the United States.[11]

If isolationism dominates, where will be America's motivation to carry out a Plan of Triage, from where will come the drive for using wisely the great power available to it during the Time of Famines?

## Obstacle No. 4: Sensitivity to Critics Abroad

The criticism of American foreign policies by foreigners is easy to understand.

Ever since the last war the majority of intellectuals in the other nations, whether in India or Switzerland, Guinea or Sweden, Paraguay or France, have professed in strident voices their disdain for America's leaders. This contempt is colored by several human factors, such as the frustration of minor powers unable to control even their own affairs in the international arena, such as envy toward the most rich and dominant world power. These political provincials do not understand action policies carried forward in the midst of international tensions. They have not been, and cannot be, a part of the policy making. When world decisions are made which will affect them, they must remain sitting on the sidelines. But it is human nature not to like being left on the outside and so they continue their criticisms while at the same time smugly drawing aside their skirts from the hard and dirty facts of international life.

There is no need here to defend American actions around the world since World War II, to admit the isolated mistakes, to emphasize the crises when, generally, American leaders made the right decisions and carried them through effectively, and to point to the kind of world we would be living in today if Washington had not stood firm in the long succession of confrontations with communism in Iran, Turkey, Greece, Berlin, Korea, Lebanon, Laos, Cuba, Dominican Republic, Vietnam. These confrontations received precious little support from the intellectuals of nations not at that moment in the cockpit of action. Their fearful, tearful advice to Washington has forever been "Do nothing!" "Do nothing!" "Don't rock the boat!" Or "What you ought to do, but don't ask any help from me to do it, is to . . ."

Important here is the group in each country that considers themselves intellectuals, for they do greatly influence their societies, especially the more primitive ones.

By intellectual I mean a literate person who feels himself a member of the educated minority. It is not actual intellectual superiority that makes the intellectual but the feeling of belonging to an intellectual elite. . . . In Asia, Africa and Latin America every student, every petty member of the professions, every clerk, feels himself equipped for national leadership. . . .

The intellectual's most fundamental incompatibility is with the masses. In every age since the invention of writing he has given words to his loathing and hatred of the common man. . . . The ruling intelligentsias in communist countries and in the new countries in Asia and Africa are treating the masses as raw material to be experimented on, processed and wasted at will. . . . Closely allied to the intellectual's attitude toward the masses is his incompatibility with America. . . . Wherever American influence penetrates, it rouses the fear and the hostility of the intellectuals . . . [because] the Americanization of a country means, above all, the stiffening of the workingman's backbone and the sharpening of his appetites. . . . [This] amounts to giving it a classless aspect, a sameness that suggests equality. It is this that the foreign intellectual fears and resents. . . .

The protagonists of our present age are not America and Russia, or America and China, or Russia and China, but America and the intellectuals. . . . A letter recently received from an American diplomat serving in Asia says: "I am always surprised at the amount of raw, venomous hatred for the U.S. that is displayed by everyone with more than six years of education in this part of the world. Strangely, the poor and illiterate masses remain well disposed toward the U.S., but that will certainly disappear with the next generation. . . . By recognizing as a constant factor the hostility of the underdeveloped intellectuals, we could avoid the costly efforts involved in trying to win world public opinion, and cold-bloodedly realize what they already know — that we are by our basic nature and destiny a subversive force in these societies, and that our own security lies in the transfer of power to the masses and to real mass leaders, not elite class leaders." [12]

One often hears of the "reservoir" of good will for the United States among the citizens of foreign countries. This indeed is a genuine thing, but it is directed toward admiration of American industrial, agricultural and technical success, admiration of the American comfort of living, appreciation of the friendliness of most Americans encountered abroad; it is not directed toward admiration of the philosophical basis of American life and it most definitely is not directed toward admiration of American leaders in Washington and the policies enacted there.

In the years ahead the leaders in Washington will be making their decisions against a background of continuous cacophony of foreign criticism and derision and with only minor support, if any, from the major countries in Europe and from the other members of The Granary. No matter how the United States uses its food power it will be criticized. If there is such an outpouring of criticism today from these same countries concerning American policies for the containment of communism, think what an outcry a Plan of Triage will stimulate! It behooves Washington to draw up such a plan with care and logic — and not to give way to undue worry about the foreign critics.

## Obstacle No. 5: Political Instability at Home

The element of never ending change is found throughout all aspects of the American life, of the American social structure — always throwing off the old, always reaching for the new. This is often praised as perhaps the most vital factor in creating our steady progress forward.

Now, however, a consistent single-mindedness is necessary to mold a program for handling our food stocks and to adhere to that program for several decades — and to do this in the face of the upheavals in the governments around the world which make a consistent policy toward them particularly difficult. This complexity is compounded because our own convictions are seldom firm regarding basic political doctrines, such as, to name one, whether to support a wobbly, noisy, left-leaning democracy or to stand behind a stable, rightist military junta.

Add to this a further complexity: science is constantly refining mass media techniques for manipulating American public opinion; increasingly now pressure groups can, scientifically, often shift American support from one policy to another within a short time.

The hardest of the hard part, however, is for Washington to maintain a steady policy when a new chief executive comes into office every four or eight years, with shiftings in congressional strength in between.

He arrives in the White House flush with the excitement of a long and arduous political campaign spent, as often as not, in lambasting his predecessor. Thus, it is both human nature and traditional politics to sweep out the old and pretend to be the dashing new man on the white horse who is going to save everything from perdition.

Is there a better example than President Kennedy? In international affairs, at least, his only considered policy, as he burst into the White House, was, it seemed, to dump everything from the old administration. The New Era Has Arrived! It was good politics for the moment because the world did accept him in his self-created image. It is difficult, however, to list any of the international policies instigated in his early days in office to replace those he was dumping that have survived. His Alliance for Progress and his Vietnam policy were both in disarray well before his death. The foreign aid program, shaky as it was before his inauguration, was further weakened by his dumping of the policies of the old technicians and replacing them with the theses of his new type of aid officials — the money men and social reformers; often their only concept of foreign aid was to give open-end development money to a country with one hand while the other tried to knock over its established social structure.

Yet President Kennedy should not be criticized for sweeping the clean broom in international affairs. It is about par for the course with new presidents; the only difference is that at least Kennedy did it with such fine panache.

The basic fact to underline is that it is easy to go dashing about changing policies in international affairs because of their innately fluid, mercurial conditions, and because it is politically safe — there are few, or none at all, powerful domestic blocs to placate; there are few controls to prevent sudden fluctuations in policy by this or that presidential favorite aide.

Our foreign aid demonstrates this changeableness. On the surface we have been consistent in that the program has always received its congressional allotments and its public support. But when David Bell took over the Agency for International Development he was the twelfth head in fourteen years. By then the Agency itself had had seven structural changes; no fewer than eight presidential committees had reviewed and studied it in depth.[13] With each new administration there has been a shifting and a vacillation in the manner in which the AID money is used. Indeed, the original technical assistance concept stressed by President Truman in Point Four of his inaugural address has long since given way to emphasis on grants and loans. The brush-fire headlines of the moment have further twisted and changed the programs as funds were rushed here and there to meet the emergencies. The façade of our foreign aid has been cast in long-range phraseology. The practice, however, has been mostly short-range, two-year projects. That is all the time the aid personnel have in which to work until new directives come out of Washington.

Thus, we have the obstacle of maintaining a Plan of Triage

through several administrations, a period when surely there will be constant external and internal battering of every part of our foreign policy. There is the extra complication of public debate on the facts of Triage. How logically and unemotionally can one argue on the floor of the Senate, with all the world watching, whether to let Tanzania starve but not Kenya? To save Tunisia but not Algeria? To save India but not raise a finger to help Africa? Yet the debate must be a public one. The decisions must represent a sincere and stable public opinion because the administration will change every few years, not merely in personnel, but often in basic philosophy.

On the plus side, of course, such an open debate will be the clearest way of telling those countries who will receive our food why they were chosen and not others — and, therefore, just what will be expected of them.

## Obstacle No. 6: The Ease of Overcommitting Our Resources

An ever present danger will be that Washington will extend America's commitments to feed the hungry nations beyond the limit of our resources.

Not only are the food stocks limited, as I keep emphasizing, but also all the rest of the range of resources. Also limited is our corps of technicians. Already many observers believe the United States has grossly overextended its political and technical commitments around the world.

Walter Lippmann says:

The real problem for [the United States] is not financial. The country can easily afford to pay for all these operations (Vietnam, the war on poverty, sending men to the moon). The real pinch comes from the fact that money will not buy enough technicians and trained men, qualified administrators and commanders, nor will it buy the morale and the attention and the variegated energy which would be needed to carry out effectively and successfully all the commitments at home and around the globe. Only those who suffer from the delusion of omnipotence will think that this country can reconstruct its own society, fight a major war in Asia, and police the world from Berlin to Korea, from Central Asia to South America.[14]

And, I add, feed all the starving in the critical years ahead.

The crucial and radical defect of policy-making in this administration [is] a habitual lack of prudence in making policy and capacity agree with one another. . . . Our European allies are not in doubt about our integrity. They are in doubt about our capacity.[15]

We think of ourselves as "good guys." As good guys we are prone to say yes when asked for a handout. Already our food aid is extended to more countries than we can possibly feed ten years from now. In the next few years retrenchment in these commitments must be made, and that will be difficult when the begging for the food in each country increases with each year.

Too many Americans in posts of authority still feel the United States has enough food to feed the world. Or they believe that *something* will come along either to expand food production overnight or to curtail population growth overnight. If such complacency continues it is certain to cause the United States to enter into ill-conceived decisions on the use of its food, to drift into easy ways out, to scatter away its food resources. Like a mother giving a crying baby a pacifier to quiet him momentarily, so may the United States tend to ship the food piecemeal to whichever country shouts the loudest.

## Obstacle No. 7: Repugnance to Forcing Other Nations to Adhere to America's Policies

Not exerting the full measure of America's strength to persuade the food-receiving nations to abide by Washington's policies for distributing the food can become a serious weakness as the Time of Famines comes down upon us.

Presumably, this will mean that Washington must take on the responsibility of telling the foreign government: If you want our food you must comply with our conditions for such help (e.g., strengthen agriculture, family planning). Should the answer be negative then that is that; we turn our attention to others.

If, however, the answer is affirmative and the food shipments are begun (shipments which will last for many years) and the receiving government fails to carry out its assumed obligations, then, surely, we have the responsibility to insist on compliance and, if necessary, to *force* compliance.

There are many forms of pressure that Washington can use to gain this cooperation — economic, social, political, diplomatic, propaganda. If Washington draws back from using these available pressures, then indeed its policies will be in danger of impotence. The responsibility for effective utilization of our food stocks must be faced up to by Washington and by the American people.

President Johnson stated in a speech: "We know now that so interwoven is our destiny with the world's destiny, so intricate are the bonds between us and every continent, that our responsibilities would be just as real in the absence of the Communist threat. For every school boy senses — what some statesmen may not yet comprehend — that responsibility is the price of power and influence." [16]

Yet he immediately reverted to the traditional American "hands off" policy by saying: "Our assistance to these nations, our involvement in their affairs, will be no greater than they choose to have it." [17]

Unfortunately, non-involvement is a role we cannot practice in the distribution of our food.

For instance, these undeveloped nations often do not have even the personnel available to draw up the technical data in support of their requests to the American government, let alone make decisions as to which action, of several alternatives, is most advisable.

Testifying before a congressional committee I said that in Latin America there are too few men qualified to know what should or can be done there in order to strengthen and modernize their agriculture. I added that this shortage of Latin American agriculturists must be compensated by our spelling out for them these gaps in their knowledge regarding how to develop this key sector of their economy.

Congressman Abraham J. Multer immediately objected to my point of view, saying, "We cannot without their request and cooperation go in and help them improve their conditions." [18] Thus, he repeated the same "hands off" restriction voiced by President Johnson and countless other officials, editorial writers and most of the American public.

Actually, both houses of Congress have periodically hankered to tie political restrictions to the successive foreign aid bills. Each time, however, pressure from the White House has removed the amendments from the final bill, or at least has watered them down to innocuousness. Typical was the original refusal of the House of Representatives to vote for the new Food for Peace bill unless it barred as recipients all nations who trade in any commodities with Cuba or North Vietnam, i.e., Egypt, Yugoslavia, Poland, India.

The value of Washington's formulating clear-cut decisions as to which countries shall receive its food and which countries shall not, such as with a Plan of Triage, is that the odious aura of charity can be eliminated. The receiving nation will know that it is not receiving the food as an act of charity but because the United States decided, after due analysis, that it can be saved from catastrophe and that it can survive the Time of Famines. In return, the receiving nation can pay for the food not with "funny money" but by putting into action those policies which will indeed make it able to survive and which some day will make it self-sufficient in food — and the two key policies must be drastic birth control programs and heavy budgetary support for the agricultural sector. The receiving nation must realize it will not be saved by American food alone, but by its own actions. The food shipments from the United States merely buy the time to allow the nation to carry out those actions.

Repugnance to force our policies on other sovereign nations is an honorable attitude in theory. In practice, it will win no battles in the War on Hunger.

Meanwhile, our agricultural lands stand ready to expand their production, to fill the storage bins and freight cars. Where will the grain be sent? To which countries? To which countries will it *not* be sent?

Only a solid, long-range policy, which includes the conditions to which the receiving nations must adhere, can assure that the food is utilized to maximum effectiveness. But it must be initiated before the Time of Famines begins.

I have listed obstacles any one of which could forestall the Americans from succeeding in leading the world during this Age of

Food, which could prevent them from even wanting to act as leader. The Age of Food brings within the grasp of the American people and of their agricultural capacity a new epoch of greatness. But to achieve this greatness each of the obstacles must be overcome.

## Now It Is America's Turn to Shape History

Athenian democracy. Roman militarianism. Byzantine imperialism. Russian czarist and commissar autocracy. British parliamentarianism.

Each endured for an era as the basis for leadership of their worlds. The reasons for endurance were different in each case, but they derived out of a basic conviction or aspiration of the body politic. The Athenians aspired to achieve personal, individual freedom. The Romans to attain glory for their city. The Byzantines to preserve civilization from the barbarians. The Russians wanted, and continue to want, the integrality of Mother Russia. The British believed implicitly their rule was beneficial for the subject peoples, the White Man's Burden. In each case economic advantage and prosperity were additional driving interests, but these were certainly not the only motivating forces which produced success.

Now it is the turn of the American people to stand trial before the tribunal of history.

The next ten years may set the course which eventually can determine how the United States will be judged.

For in this period the American people must deliberately take on a role of leadership that will inspire and guide the stricken world through the complex Time of Famines. The United States must not lose the future by default.

The onrushing hunger of the world can be the stimulation, the catalyst, which will spur the continuation of our traditional dynamism. The Time of Famines can be the American twentieth-century dragon to slay.

To do so we must today build up our food reserves, lay the framework for distributing the food within a Plan of Triage, and tailor our commitments to fit the size of our resources.

Today we are a dynamic nation. It is well within our capabilities to work out policies which will alleviate the hunger and which will offer to some of our fellow nations, if not all, time to create their "better" world when the famines have subsided.

The majority of today's nations, and not only the new ones, have never had the chance to create their own form of life, to generate the flowering of their own personality.

Let history's tribunal record that, although the United States could not prevent the Time of Famines, it nevertheless accepted this period as a challenge to its ingenuity and power. Let history record that because the American people met this challenge, the Time of Famines was something more than a crisis in man's development, that out of the experience of the Time of Famines came the foundation on which man built an era of greatness, an era of greatness not for the United States alone but also for the hungry nations.

# References

## CHAPTER 1

1. Orville L. Freeman, Secretary of Agriculture, address at the United Nations Biennial Conference of the Food and Agriculture Organization, Rome, Nov. 23, 1965.
2. Ronald Freedman, president, Population Association of America, *New York Times*, Apr. 24, 1965.
3. Roger Revelle, director, Harvard Center for Population Studies, "The University Population Center," *Harvard Public Health Alumni Bull.* (Jan. 1965), p. 15.
4. *World War on Hunger*, Hearings before the House Committee on Agriculture, 89th Cong., 2d Sess., on H.R. 12152, H.R. 12704, and H.R. 12785, Feb. 14, 1966, p. 23.
5. Rep. Harold D. Cooley, as quoted by Felix Belair, Jr., *New York Times*, Feb. 23, 1966.
6. Editorial, *New Statesman*, Jan. 21, 1966, p. 69.
7. *Time*, May 6, 1966.
8. Population Reference Bureau, Washington, D.C., *World Population Data Sheet*, Dec. 1965.
9. United Nations, Department of Economic and Social Affairs, *Provisional Report on World Population Prospects as Assessed in 1963* (1964), p. 120.
10. Ibid.
11. Population Reference Bureau, press release, Dec. 7, 1964.
12. United Nations, Department of Economic and Social Affairs, *World Population Prospects up to the Year 2000* (1965).
13. MacFarlane Burnet, *Natural History of Infections and Diseases*, 3d ed. (Cambridge: Harvard Univ. Press, 1962), p. 308.
14. Warren S. Thompson, *The Population Ahead*, ed. Roy G. Francis (Minneapolis: Univ. of Minnesota Press, 1958), p. 126.
15. *Population Bulletin of the United Nations*, No. 6 (1962), p. 17; and Population Reference Bureau, *World Population Data Sheet*, Dec. 1965.
16. *The Growth of World Population*, National Academy of Sciences — National Research Council Publication 1091 (1963), p. 10.
17. Population Reference Bureau, *World Population Data Sheet*, Dec. 1965.
18. Ibid.
19. U. S. Department of Health, Education and Welfare, *Vital Statistics Indicators* (Feb. 1966).
20. Jean Mayer, "Food and Population: The Wrong Problem?," *Daedalus* (Summer, 1964), p. 834.
21. *Washington Post*, June 4, 1963.
22. Irene B. Taeuber, "Population Growth in Latin America: Paradox of Development," *Population Bull.*, Vol. 18 (Oct. 1962), p. 128.

23. United Nations, Department of Economic and Social Affairs, *Provisional Report on World Population Prospects as Assessed in 1963* (1964), p. 120.
24. Ansley J. Cole and Edgar M. Hoover, *Population Growth and Economic Development in Low-Income Countries* (Princeton: Princeton Univ. Press, 1958).
25. J. Mayone Stycos, "Problems of Fertility Control in Under-Developed Areas: Marriage and Family Living," in *Population, Evolution, Birth Control*, ed. Garrett Hardin (San Francisco: W. H. Freeman, 1965), p. 321.
26. Lee Rainwater, *Family Design, Marital Sexuality, Family Size and Contraception* (Chicago: Aldine, 1965), p. 120.
27. Ibid.
28. Roger Revelle in *World War on Hunger*, Hearings before the House Committee on Agriculture, 89th Cong., 2d Sess., on H.R. 12152, H.R. 12704, and H.R. 12785, Feb. 14, 1966, p. 41.
29. Alan F. Guttmacher, statement before the Senate Subcommittee on Foreign Aid Expenditures of the Committee on Government Operations, 89th Cong., 1st Sess., on S. 1676, Aug. 10, 1965.
30. *Washington Post*, Aug. 8, 1965.
31. Calculated on the basis of a 2.4% annual increase in a population of 482 million, taken from *World Population Data Sheet* (see n. 8 above).
32. Population Crisis Committee, Washington, D.C., "Birth Control Expert Reports on Family Planning in India," news release, June 21, 1966.
33. Ibid.
34. Kasturi Rangan, *New York Times*, Jan. 24, 1966.
35. Ibid.
36. Robert W. Gillespie, *Family Planning on Taiwan* (New York: Population Council, Apr. 1965), p. 7.
37. Population Council, *Studies in Family Planning No. 6* (Mar. 1965).
38. Gillespie, p. 7.
39. Byung Moo Lee and John Isbister, "The Impact of Birth Control Programs on Fertility," in *Family Planning and Population Programs*, ed. Bernard Berelson et al. (Chicago: Univ. of Chicago Press, 1965), p. 740.
40. Leo F. Schnore, "Social Problems in the Underdeveloped Areas: An Ecological View," *Social Problems*, Vol. VIII (Winter, 1961), p. 187.
41. *Washington Post*, Feb. 20, 1966.
42. S. Chandrasekhar, "A Billion Indians by 2000 A.D.?," *New York Times Magazine*, Apr. 4, 1965.
43. Population Council, *Studies in Family Planning No. 9* (Jan. 1966).
44. Ibid.
45. Ibid.
46. *New York Times*, Apr. 24, 1965.
47. All population density figures are from Agency for International Development, Statistics and Reports Division, *Selected Economic Data for the Less Developed Countries* (June 1965).
48. *El Diario de Hoy*, San Salvador, Jan. 25, 1962, as quoted by J. Mayone Stycos, "Opinions of Latin American Intellectuals on Population Problems and Birth Control," *Annals of the American Academy of Political and Social Science*, Vol. 360 (July 1965), p. 19.
49. Irene B. Taeuber, *The Population of Japan* (Princeton: Princeton Univ. Press, 1958).
50. For the source of these percentages, see n. 47.

51. Taeuber, p. 90.
52. United Nations, *Statistical Year Book* (1964).
53. Drew Pearson, *Washington Post*, Nov. 30, 1965.
54. K. S. Sundara Rajan, address before the Committee on the World Food Crisis, Washington, D.C., Dec. 9, 1965.
55. Robert C. Cook, president, Population Reference Bureau, Washington, D.C., in conversation with the author, Aug. 30, 1966.
56. J. Mayone Stycos, "Obstacles to Programs of Population Control — Facts and Fancies," *Marriage and Family Living* (Feb. 1965), p. 6.
57. Dexter L. Hanley, statement before the Senate Subcommittee on Foreign Aid Expenditures of the Committee on Government Operations, 89th Cong., 1st Sess., on S. 1676, Aug. 24, 1965.
58. Brock Chisholm, "Dangerous Complacency Toward Biological Warfare," *The Humanist* (Jan.-Feb. 1960), p. 15.
59. *New York Times*, May 19, 1966.
60. *International Development Review*, Vol. 3, No. 6 (June 15, 1966).
61. Henry Giniger, *New York Times*, June 8, 1966.
62. Population Reference Bureau, *World Population Data Sheet*, Dec. 1965.
63. *New York Times*, Jan. 2, 1966.
64. Lester R. Brown, address before the Pacific Northwest Farm Forum. Spokane, Wash., Feb. 8, 1966.
65. Robert Cassen, *New Statesman*, Jan. 21, 1966, p. 96.
66. Appendix to testimony by Thomas Ware before the Senate Subcommittee on Economic and Social Policy of the Foreign Relations Committee, June 29, 1965.

## CHAPTER 2

1. Orville L. Freeman, Secretary of Agriculture, address at the United Nations Biennial Conference of the Food and Agriculture Organization, Rome, Nov. 23, 1965.
2. U.S. Department of Agriculture, *Changes in Agriculture in 26 Developing Nations 1948-1963*, Foreign Agricultural Economic Report No. 27 (Nov. 1965).
3. Quentin M. West, *World Food Needs*, Foreign Regional Analysis Division, Economic Research Service, U.S. Department of Agriculture, Feb. 10, 1966, p. 10.
4. Carl O. Winberg, "Indonesia Having Trouble Maintaining Its Copra Exports," *Foreign Agriculture*, Nov. 9, 1964.
5. Ibid.
6. Lester R. Brown, *Man, Land and Food*, U.S. Department of Agriculture, FAE Report No. 11 (Nov. 1963), p. 76.
7. B. R. Sen, director general of Food and Agriculture Organization, United Nations, Circular Letter No. 90 to Ministers of Agriculture, Aug. 1965.
8. Bernard D. Nossiter, *Washington Post*, Oct. 13, 1966.
9. United Nations, Food and Agriculture Organization, *The State of Food and Agriculture 1965*, p. 72.
10. A synthesis of several *Agricultural Statistics Yearbooks*, U.S. Dept. of Agriculture.
11. Brown, op. cit., pp. 53 and 56.
12. Thomas E. Street, Deputy Assistant Administrator for Export Programs,

Foreign Agricultural Service, U.S. Department of Agriculture, in a letter to the author, June 27, 1966.

13. *Food for Peace 1964 Annual Report on Public Law 480,* House Document No. 130-89/1 (Washington, D.C.; Government Printing Office, Mar. 1965).

14. Paul C. Tullier, "Population Boom . . . or Boomerang," *The 1964 World Book Yearbook* (Chicago: Field Enterprises Educational Corp., 1964), p. 200.

15. *New York Times,* July 10, 1966.

16. Hedrick Smith, *New York Times,* Jan. 29, 1966.

17. *New York Times,* July 10, 1966.

18. See n. 12.

19. See n. 2.

20. Raymond Ewell, vice-president for research, State University of New York at Buffalo, in a letter to the author, July 18, 1966.

21. Ritchie Calder, *Common Sense about a Starving World* (London: Macmillan, 1962), p. 15.

22. Brown, op. cit., p. 38.

23. Frank C. Consolazio, LeRoy C. Matoush, Richard A. Nelson, Juan B. Torres and Gerhart J. Isaac, "Environmental Temperature and Energy Expenditures," *Journal of Applied Physiology* (Jan. 1963), pp. 65-68.

24. Adapted from Table II-2, United Nations, Food and Agriculture Organization, *The State of Food and Agriculture 1965,* p. 15.

25. United Nations, Department of Economic and Social Affairs, *Provisional Report on World Population Prospects as Assessed in 1963* (1964).

26. Adapted from "Table of Recommended Dietary Allowances," National Research Council Publication No. 1146 (1964), p. vii.

27. Brown, op. cit., p. 41.

28. Calculated from figures in Robert C. Cook's "World Population Projections, 1965-2000," *Population Bull.* (Oct. 1965), pp. 96-97.

29. "Famine Is Here," *New Republic,* Sept. 18, 1965.

30. Ibid.

31. Ibid.

32. Ibid.

33. Raymond Ewell, "Famine and Fertilizer," *Chemical and Engineering News* (Dec. 14, 1964), pp. 106-117.

34. Roger Revelle, *World War on Hunger,* Hearings before the House Committee on Agriculture, 89th Cong., 2d Sess., on H.R. 12152, H.R. 12704, and H.R. 12785, Feb. 14, 1966.

35. *Report on India's Food Crisis and Steps to Meet It* (sponsored by the Ford Foundation but published by the Government of India, Delhi, Apr. 1959), pp. 1, 3, 14.

36. Charles E. Lindblom, "Has India an Economic Future?," *Foreign Affairs,* Vol. 44 (1966), p. 240.

37. Ibid.

38. *Newsweek,* Nov. 23, 1964.

39. Horace J. Davis, U.S. Agricultural Attaché in India, "India's Food Grain Situation," *Foreign Agriculture* (Nov. 2, 1964), p. 3.

40. Lindblom, op. cit., p. 240.

41. Lester R. Brown, staff economist, U.S. Department of Agriculture, in conversation with the author, Sept. 21, 1965.

42. *Newsweek,* Nov. 23, 1964.
43. Ibid.
44. George K. Parman, executive secretary, Committee on Marine Protein Resource Development, Food and Nutrition Board, National Academy of Sciences, Washington, D.C., in a letter to the author, July 12, 1966.
45. *U.S. News and World Report,* Oct. 12, 1964.
46. Ibid.
47. V. M. Tandon, "India's Food Outlook Brighter," *Foreign Agriculture,* Apr. 5, 1965.
48. Ibid.
49. Selig S. Harrison, *Washington Post,* Aug. 22, 1965.
50. Editorial, *Washington Post,* Aug. 14, 1965.
51. See note 41 above.
52. See note 25 above.
53. Raymond Ewell, *World War on Hunger,* Hearings before the House Committee on Agriculture, 89th Cong., 2d Sess., on H.R. 12152, H.R. 12704, and H.R. 12785, Feb. 16, 1966, p. 139.
54. Ibid.
55. Felix Belair, Jr., *New York Times,* Feb. 18, 1966.
56. Herschel D. Newsom, testimony before the Senate Committee on Agriculture and Forestry, 89th Cong., 2d Sess., on S. 2157, S. 2826, S. 2932, S. 2933, S. 2995, and H.R. 14929, Mar. 4, 1966, p. 126.
57. Orville L. Freeman, Secretary of Agriculture, address before the Fifth Annual High-Level Meeting of the OECD, Development Assistance Committee, Washington, D.C., July 21, 1966.

## CHAPTER 3

1. As quoted by Milan Kubic in a letter to the author, Apr. 26, 1966.
2. *National Citizens Commission Report on Committee for Agriculture and Food* for the White House Conference on International Cooperation, Dec. 1, 1965.
3. Richard T. Hanna, address before the House of Representatives, 89th Cong., Jan. 12, 1966.
4. Archibald T. McPherson, "Chemistry, Food and Civilization," *Journal,* Washington Academy of Sciences, Feb. 1959, p. 6.
5. *Holland Herald,* Vol. 1, No. 3 (1966), p. 23.
6. Burt Schorr, *Wall Street Journal,* July 6, 1966.
7. LeRoy Voris, executive secretary, Food and Nutrition Board, National Academy of Sciences, in conversation with the author, Feb. 16, 1966.
8. Howard W. Mattson, "Food for the Starving," *International Science and Technology,* Dec. 1965.
9. George Parman, Food and Nutrition Board Staff, National Academy of Sciences, in conversation with the author, Nov. 18, 1965.
10. Mattson, op. cit.
11. Schorr, op. cit.
12. "U.S. Business vs. Malthus," *Forbes,* Mar. 1, 1966, p. 26.
13. Harold Milner, "Now — Bread from the Sea," *Collier's,* Apr. 16, 1954.
14. *Business Week,* July 31, 1965.
15. *Business Week,* Oct. 16, 1965.
16. Ibid.

17. Glen T. Seaborg, "Nuclear Energy for the Benefit of Man," *Department of State Bulletin*, Oct. 12, 1964, p. 521.
18. Hugh Nicol, "Facts about Food Supplies," *Food Technology*, Mar. 1960, p. 15.
19. Wilbert McLeod Chapman, Testimony before the Senate Committee on Commerce, on hearings on National Oceanographic Council, 89th Cong., 1st Sess., on S-944, Apr. 12, 1965.
20. Wilbert McLeod Chapman in *Proceedings, 14th Annual Meeting*, Agriculture Research Institute, Oct. 18-19, 1965, National Academy of Sciences–National Research Council, Washington, D.C., pp. 65-94.
21. Joseph E. King, Bureau of Commercial Fisheries, Dept. of Interior, by telephone, June 21, 1966.
22. Herman Einarsson, "Peru's Giddy Anchovy-Hunt," *New Scientist*, June 17, 1965.
23. Ibid.
24. Howard W. Mattson, "Food for the World," *International Science and Technology*, Dec. 1965, pp. 28-39.
25. J. George Harrar, president of the Rockefeller Foundation, Testimony before the House Committee on Agriculture, 89th Cong., 1st Sess., Feb. 16, 1966.
26. *Federal Funds for Research and Development and Other Scientific Activities, Fiscal Years 1963, -64, -65*, Vol. 13 (National Science Foundation Publication No. 65-13), pp. 179-180.
27. "Thailand Reports a Corn Boom," *Front Lines* (Agency for International Development publication), Mar. 15, 1965.
28. Norman E. Borlaug, director, International Wheat Improvement Program, Rockefeller Foundation, address before the 56th Annual Meeting of the American Phytopathological Society, Lafayette, Ind., Aug. 24, 1965; reprinted in *Phytopathology* Vol. 55, No. 10 (Oct. 1965), p. 1090.
29. Ibid., p. 1089.
30. Editorial, "Science: A Catalyst for Emergent Countries," *Nature*, Jan. 25, 1964.
31. Ibid.
32. John Rouleau, Office of International Scientific and Technological Affairs, U.S. Department of State, by telephone June 15, 1966.
33. Joseph L. Newman, deputy director, AID information staff, by telephone June 7, 1966.
34. Borlaug, op. cit., p. 1096.
35. J. George Harrar, president, the Rockefeller Foundation, address before the Sixth International Congress of Nutrition, Edinburgh, Aug. 9, 1963.
36. Virgil A. Johnson, U.S. Department of Agriculture, address before the Fourth International Cereal and Bread Congress, Vienna, May 23, 1966.
37. W. W. Bryan, senior agronomist, Tropical Grassland Institute, Brisbane, Australia, in correspondence with the author, Oct. 4, 1965.
38. Frank W. Parker, Technical Cooperation and Research, AID, in address before the Conference on Changes in Fertilizer Distribution and Marketing, Tennessee Valley Authority, Oct. 6, 1965.
39. *The Quiet Revolution*, Skokie, Ill.: International Minerals and Chemical Corp., 1965.
40. Forrest Hill, vice-president, Ford Foundation, during briefing of NAS

# References

255

Task Force for the Selection of Research-Educational Institutions for Tropical America, U.S. Department of State, Washington, Oct. 20, 1964.
41. Theodore W. Schultz, *Economic Crises in World Agriculture* (University of Michigan Press, 1965), p. 49.
42. Ibid., pp. 50-51.
43. Lester R. Brown, *Man, Land and Food*, FAE Report No. 11, Department of Agriculture, Nov. 1963, p. 106.
44. Ibid.
45. *Kansas City Star*, Oct. 24, 1965.
46. Walter H. Pawley, Freedom from Hunger Campaign, Basic Study No. 10, 1963.
47. *Congressional Record*, May 16, 1960.
48. Lawrence Galton, "The World Is Getting Thirstier," *New York Times Magazine*, Sept. 27, 1964.
49. United Nations, *Statistics of Hunger*, p. 6.
50. "Analysis of Factors Associated with Differences and Changes in Agricultural Production in Underdeveloped Countries," Third Progress Report on Participating Agency Agreements between AID and ERS, Department of Agriculture, July 20, 1965, p. 27.
51. Ibid., p. 60.
52. Brown, op. cit., p. 93.
53. Lester R. Brown, "Population Growth, Food Needs and Population Problems," *World Population and Food Supplies*, American Society of Agronomy, Special Number, Feb. 1965.
54. Mary McNeil, "Lateritic Soils," *Scientific American*, Nov. 1964, pp. 97-102.
55. Frank A. Pearson and Floyd A. Harper, *The World's Hunger* (New York: Cornell University Press, 1945).
56. W. S. Woytinsky and E. S. Woytinsky, *World Population and Production* (New York: 20th Century Fund, 1953), p. 319.
57. *Diario de Pernambuco*, Aug. 20, 1963.
58. *Washington Post*, Jan. 9, 1963.
59. *Washington Post*, Feb. 28, 1966.
60. *New York Times*, Mar. 14, 1965.
61. *Marketing*, USDA Yearbook in Agriculture (Washington, D.C.: Government Printing Office, 1954), p. 159.
62. Duncan Norton-Taylor, "What the U.S. Can Do about World Hunger," *Fortune*, June 1966, p. 112.
63. Ibid., p. 180.
64. Ibid., p. 184.
65. Ibid., p. 112.
66. Raymond Ewell, Testimony before the Senate Subcommittee on Foreign Aid Expenditures of the Committee on Government Operations on S. 1676, 89th Cong., 1st Sess., Feb. 9, 1966.
67. Marquis Childs, *Washington Post*, July 19, 1965.

## CHAPTER 4

1. I. R. Sinai, *The Challenge of Modernisation: The West's Impact on the Non-Western World* (New York: Norton, 1964), p. 54.

2. Edith Hamilton, *The Roman Way* (New York: Norton 1932), p. 269.
3. *Newsweek*, Aug. 9, 1965, p. 46.
4. Population Reference Bureau, Washington, D.C., *World Population Data Sheet*, Dec. 1965.
5. *Food Balance for 30 Countries in Africa and West Asia, 1959-61*, ERS Foreign 119, U.S. Department of Agriculture, 1965, p. 3.
6. "The Passions and Perils of Nationhood," *Time*, March 11, 1966, p. 38.
7. "For the Child Who Has Nothing," *The New Republic*, Dec. 26, 1964, p. 7.
8. Robert S. McNamara, Secretary of Defense, address before the American Society of Newspaper Editors, Montreal, Canada, May 18, 1966.
9. Ibid.
10. Ibid.
11. Robert Clotworthy, swimming coach, Princeton University, "Report to the Mexican Swimming Federation," Sept. 1965.
12. Sinai, op. cit., p. 176.
13. "Brazil: Government by the Consent of the Military," *The New Republic*, Apr. 16, 1966, p. 18.
14. Quoted from *East Africa Royal Commissions, 1953-1955 Report*, by Montague Yudelman in *Africans on the Land* (Cambridge: Harvard University Press, 1964), p. 11.

CHAPTER 5

1. Karl Hobson, extension economist, Washington State University, "The Wheat Shortage Is Here," *Farm Journal*, Aug. 1966, p. 21.
2. Seeley G. Lodwick, Testimony before the House Committee on Agriculture, 89th Cong., 2nd Sess., Mar. 9, 1966, p. 486.
3. Louis H. Bean, "Closing the Nutritional Gap," in *Food and People*, study paper prepared by the Subcommittee on Foreign Economic Policy of the Joint Economic Committee, 87th Cong., 1st Sess., Nov. 30, 1961, pp. 31-74.
4. Lester R. Brown, *Man, Land and Food*, FAE Report No. 11, Department of Agriculture, Nov. 1963, p. 48.
5. Ibid., p. 66.
6. See n. 1.
7. Brown, op. cit. Data from p. 89 adapted by author.
8. Quentin M. West, *World Food Needs*, Foreign Regional Analysis Division, Economic Research Service, U.S. Department of Agriculture, Feb. 10, 1966, p. 18.
9. *Handbook of Agricultural Charts*, Department of Agriculture Handbook No. 300, 1965, p. 61.
10. Lester R. Brown, address before the Pacific Northwest Farm Forum, Spokane, Feb. 8, 1966, p. 10.
11. Calculated by the author on the basis of a 42% increase in dollar sales of agricultural exports sold in the six-year period 1960-1965 as appears in testimony by Raymond Ioanes, Administrator for Foreign Agricultural Service, Department of Agriculture, before the House Subcommittee on Department of Agriculture and Related Agencies Appropriations of the Committee on Appropriations, 89th Cong., 2nd Sess., Feb. 23, 1966 (p. 16, pt. 3).

12. Lyle P. Schertz and Richard J. Cannon, "U.S. Wheat Paramount in World Supply Situation," *Foreign Agriculture*, Mar. 7, 1966.
13. "World Food Program May Continue," *Foreign Agriculture*, May 3, 1965.
14. *Foreign Agriculture*, Jan. 31, 1966.
15. *Washington Post*, Mar. 3, 1966.
16. "Food for Freedom Program and Commodity Reserves," Hearings before the Senate Committee on Agriculture and Forestry, 89th Cong., 2d Sess., on S. 2157, S. 2826, S. 2932, S. 2933, S. 2995 and H.R. 14929, March 2, 3, 4, 7, 8 and June 15, 1966, p. 59.
17. Ibid., p. 134.
18. Georg Borgstrom, *Hungry Planet* (New York: Macmillan, 1965), p. 357.
19. *Foreign Agriculture*, Mar. 7, 1966.
20. Agriculture Appropriations Hearings for 1967, pp. 46-67 (see n. 11).
21. *Handbook of Agricultural Charts*, p. 66.
22. Borgstrom, op. cit., p. 349.
23. Ibid.
24. "World War on Hunger," Hearings before the House Committee on Agriculture, 89th Cong., 2nd Sess., Feb. 14-18, 1966, p. 192.
25. Orville L. Freeman, Secretary of Agriculture, "Food for Freedom Program and Commodity Reserves," Hearings, p. 24 (see n. 16).
26. Ibid., p. 32.
27. "Food for Freedom," joint release of Departments of State and Agriculture, Feb. 10, 1966, p. 16.
28. Orville L. Freeman, Secretary of Agriculture, "World War on Hunger," Hearings, p. 192 (see n. 24).
29. Calculated for the author by Charles A. Gibbons, U.S. Dept. of Agriculture economist, using data to be published Jan. 4, 1967, in *The World Agricultural Situation, Review of 1966 and Outlook for 1967*, USDA Foreign Agricultural Economic Report No. 33 (Washington, D.C., Government Printing Office).
30. Orville L. Freeman, "World War on Hunger," Hearings, p. 193 (see n. 24).
31. Senator Herman Talmadge, "Food for Freedom Program and Commodity Reserves," Hearings, p. 132 (see n. 16).
32. Don Paarlberg, in address before the 12th Annual Meeting, Agricultural Research Institute, NAS, Washington, D.C., Oct. 18, 1963.
33. "World War on Hunger," Hearings, p. 192 (see n. 24).
34. Senator George McGovern, "Food for Freedom Program and Commodity Reserves," Hearings, p. 31 (see n. 16).

## CHAPTER 6

1. Thomas Ware, chairman of Freedom from Hunger Foundation and chairman of International Minerals and Chemical Corp., Testimony before the Senate Consultative Subcommittee on Economic and Social Affairs of the Committee on Foreign Relations, 89th Cong., 1st Sess., June 29, 1965.
2. *U.S. News and World Report*, Sept. 13, 1965, p. 44.
3. *The USSR and Eastern Europe Agricultural Situation, Review of 1965*

*and Outlook for 1966*, Economic Research Service Foreign 151, U.S. Department of Agriculture, Mar. 1966, p. 17.
4. *U.S. News and World Report*, Sept. 13, 1965, p. 45.
5. See n. 3.
6. *U.S. News and World Report*, Sept. 13, 1965, p. 45.
7. *U.S. News and World Report*, Nov. 8, 1965.
8. *Business Week*, Aug. 21, 1965, p. 30.
9. Raymond H. Anderson, *New York Times*, June 21, 1966.
10. John A. Schnittker, Under Secretary of Agriculture, address before the National Catholic Rural Life Conference, October 15, 1966.
11. Madeleine G. Kalb, "Khrushchev's Economic Problems," *The Reporter*, Dec. 20, 1962, p. 21.
12. Ibid.
13. Headline from *Miami Herald*, Mar. 5, 1962.
14. Editorial, *New York Times*, May 29, 1966.
15. Ibid.
16. "Better Red than Well-Fed," *Forbes*, Nov. 15, 1964, p. 15.
17. Editorial, *Washington Post*, Oct. 28, 1964.
18. Theodore Shabad, *New York Times*, Oct. 24, 1964.
19. E. W. Caspari and R. E. Marshak, "The Rise and Fall of Lysenko," *Science*, Vol. 149 (July 16, 1965), p. 276.
20. *U.S. News and World Report*, Sept. 13, 1965, p. 43.
21. *The USSR and Eastern Europe Agricultural Situation, Review of 1965 and Outlook for 1966*, Economic Research Service, Foreign 151, U.S. Department of Agriculture, Mar. 1966, and author's conversation Sept. 1, 1966, with G. Stanley Brown, Chief of Europe and Soviet Union, ERS, U.S. Department of Agriculture.
22. *The Economist* (London), June 25, 1966, p. 1404.
23. Harry Walters, Europe and Soviet Union, Economic Research Service, U.S. Department of Agriculture, in conversation with author, June 14, 1966.
24. Ansel S. Wood, "The Soviet Farm Crisis — and American Wheat," *Foreign Agriculture*, Aug. 10, 1964, p. 4.
25. *The USSR and Eastern Europe Agricultural Situation*, p. 60.
26. David Binder, *New York Times*, Sept. 12, 1965.
27. Ruth Sheldon Knowles, "An Economy in Shackles," *Petroleum Today* (Spring 1963).
28. Ibid.
29. "A Gloomy Castro Faces More Economic Woes," *Business Week*, June 25, 1966, p. 58.
30. Paul Hofmann, "Cuba Is in Fidel's Shirt Pocket," *New York Times Magazine*, June 13, 1965, p. 89.
31. *New York Times*, Jan. 5, 1964.
32. Ibid.
33. Ibid.
34. Kenneth A. Walker, *Planning in Chinese Agriculture: Socialization and the Private Sector* (Chicago: Aldine, 1965).
35. Robert Keatley, *Wall Street Journal*, July 25, 1966, p. 20.
36. Richard Halloran, *Washington Post*, Sept. 7, 1965.
37. Raymond A. Ioanes, "Communist Wheat-Buying Now a Big Factor in World Trade," *Foreign Agriculture*, July 12, 1965, p. 4.

38. Francis P. Hoeber, "The Economy Behind the Bamboo Curtain," *Stanford Research Institute Journal*, Mar. 1966, p. 28.
39. Lucian W. Pye, "Coming Dilemmas for China's Leaders," *Foreign Affairs*, Apr. 1966, p. 401.
40. James Reston, *New York Times*, Jan. 15, 1965.
41. Walt W. Rostow, *Prospects of Communist China* (New York: Wiley, 1954), p. 528.


CHAPTER 7

1. David Bell, Testimony before the House Committee on Agriculture, 89th Cong., 2nd Sess., on H.R. 12152, H.R. 12784, and H.R. 12785 ("World War on Hunger"), Feb. 24, 1966.
2. Norman Sklarewitz, *Wall Street Journal*, June 7, 1966.
3. Carmel Cavanaugh, Information Office, Food for Peace, by telephone to the author, Aug. 10, 1966, and "Food for Peace Act of 1966," U.S. Senate Report No. 1527, 89th Cong., 2nd Sess., p. 3.
4. Don Paarlberg in an address before the 12th Annual Meeting, Agricultural Research Institute, National Academy of Sciences, Washington, D.C., Oct. 18, 1963.
5. "Commodity Credit Corporation," *Encyclopaedia Britannica Yearbook 1955.*
6. Drew Pearson, *Washington Post*, June 17, 1966.
7. "Food for Freedom Program and Commodity Reserves," Hearings of the Senate Committee on Agriculture and Forestry, 89th Cong., 2nd Sess., on S. 2157, S. 2826, S. 2932, S. 2933, S. 2995 and H.R. 14929, Mar. 2, 1966, p. 68.
8. John Crosby, *New York Herald Tribune*, Apr. 17, 1964.
9. Robert P. Camalier, Agricultural Stabilization and Conservation Service, Department of Agriculture, by telephone to the author.
10. *Food for Peace 1964 Annual Report on Public Law 480*, House Document No. 130-89/1 (Washington, D.C.: Government Printing Office, Mar. 1965), p. 83.
11. Fred W. Devine, deputy director, CARE, "Food for Freedom and Commodity Reserves," Hearings, p. 291 (see n. 7).
12. Warren H. Leonard, professor of agronomy, Colorado State University, in correspondence with the author, July 7, 1964.
13. Hearings before the House Subcommittee on Appropriations for the Department of Agriculture for 1967, 89th Cong., 2nd Sess., Feb. 3, 1966.
14. M. J. Norton, director, Special Services, and M. R. Garstang, general counsel, National Milk Producers Federation, "Food for Freedom and Commodity Reserves," Hearings, p. 85 (see n. 7).
15. Senator Stuart Symington, during Hearings of Senate Committee on Foreign Relations, 89th Cong., 1st Sess., Mar. 19, 1965, p. 339.
16. "World Hunger: Enemy of U.S. Prosperity," *Forbes*, Mar. 1, 1966.
17. *Time*, Feb. 25, 1966.
18. T. Graydon Upton, executive vice president of the Inter-American Development Bank, in an address before the Alabama Export Council, Nov. 11, 1966.
19. Orville L. Freeman, Secretary of Agriculture, Testimony before the

House Committee on Agriculture, 89th Cong., 2nd Sess., Feb. 23, 1966 (see n. 1).

20. *National Observer*, Feb. 1, 1965.
21. Dean Rusk, "Food for Freedom Program and Commodity Reserves," Hearings, p. 232 (see n. 7).
22. Karl Hobson, extension economist, Washington State University, "Wheat Shortage Is Here," *Farm Journal*, Aug. 1966, p. 47.
23. *Food for Peace 1964 Annual Report*, pp. 83-84 (see n. 10).
24. William H. Avery, Governor of Kansas, in address before the organizational meeting of the Committee on the World Food Crisis, Washington, D.C., Dec. 9, 1965.
25. "U.S. Business vs. Malthus," *Forbes*, Mar. 1, 1966, p. 26.
26. James G. Patton, president, National Farmers Union, in address before Farmers Union Convention, St. Paul, Nov. 29, 1965 (as reported in press release by National Farmers Union of same date).
27. Harold D. Cooley, "World War on Hunger," Remarks in the House of Representatives, Jan. 25, 1966.

## CHAPTER 8

1. "World War on Hunger," Hearings before the House Committee on Agriculture, 89th Cong., 2nd Sess., on H.R. 12152, H.R. 12784, and H.R. 12785, Feb. 23, 24, 25, 1966, p. 181.
2. Ibid., p. 194.
3. *Changes in Agriculture in 26 Developing Nations 1948-1963*, Foreign Agricultural Economic Report No. 27, U.S. Department of Agriculture, Nov. 1965, p. 17.
4. "World War on Hunger," p. 182 (see n. 1).
5. Ibid., p. 180-181.
6. Ibid., p. 278.
7. Ibid., p. 286.
8. Ibid., p. 257.
9. Ibid., p. 248-249.
10. Ibid., p. 278.
11. Ibid., p. 229-230.
12. Ibid., p. 232.
13. Ibid., p. 269, 271.
14. Ibid., p. 280-281.
15. Ibid., p. 207.
16. Ibid., p. 202.
17. Ibid., p. 264.
18. Ibid., p. 290.
19. Ibid., p. 236.
20. Ibid., p. 190.
21. Ibid., p. 261.
22. Ibid., p. 189.
23. Ibid., p. 195.
24. Ibid., p. 279.
25. Ibid., p. 290.
26. Ibid., p. 283.
27. Ibid., p. 187.

28. *Wall Street Journal,* May 19, 1966.
29. Harold D. Cooley, "Industry's Role in the World War on Hunger," *Limestone* (quarterly publication of the National Limestone Institute), Spring 1966, p. 13.
30. Ibid.
31. Dean Rusk, Secretary of State, "World War on Hunger," Hearings, p. 276 (see n. 1).


CHAPTER 9

1. President Lyndon B. Johnson, message to the 89th Cong., Feb. 10, 1966.
2. Karl Hobson, "The Wheat Shortage Is Here," *Farm Journal,* Aug. 1966, p. 47.
3. *Selected Economic Data for the Less Developed Countries,* Statistics and Reports Division, Agency for International Development, Washington, D.C., June 1965.
4. Ibid.
5. Population Reference Bureau, *World Population Data Sheet* (Washington, D.C., Dec. 1965).
6. "World Hunger," *Fortune,* June 1966, p. 114.
7. *Food for Peace 1964 Annual Report on Public Law 480,* H. Doc. No. 130-89/1, (Washington, D.C.: Government Printing Office, Mar. 1965), p. 102.
8. Drew Pearson, *Washington Post,* June 17, 1966.
9. *Statistical Year Book,* United Nations, 1964.
10. *World Population Data Sheet* (see n. 6).
11. Robert Parker, "The World Food Crisis," *Farm Quarterly,* Spring 1966, pp. 52-55, 109-115.
12. See n. 4.
13. *Food for Peace 1965 Annual Report on Public Law 480,* H. Doc. No. 457-89/2, June 1966, pp. 127, 154.
14. John Ross in *Family Planning and Population Programs,* ed. Bernard Berelson et al. (Chicago: Univ. of Chicago Press, 1965).
15. See n. 4.
16. See n. 6.
17. See n. 4.
18. Norman Sklarewitz, *Wall Street Journal,* June 7, 1966.
19. Figure combined from data received from Office of Economic Officer, Indian Desk, U.S. Department of State, and the "Special Report Prepared for the House Foreign Affairs Committee on U.S. Overseas Loans and Grants and Assistance from International Organizations, Obligations and Loan Authorizations, July 1, 1945 – June 30, 1965," Office of Program Coordination, Statistics and Reports Division, AID, Mar. 18, 1966.
20. See n. 6.
21. Enver Adil in *Family Planning and Population Programs,* ed. Bernard Berelson et al. (Chicago: Univ. of Chicago Press, 1965), p. 125.
22. Ignacio Narváez and Norman E. Borlaug, "Accelerated Wheat Improvement in West Pakistan, and the Revolution in Agriculture," *Progress Report,* submitted to the Pakistan Secretary of Agriculture, Lahore, Mar. 30, 1966.

23. Ibid.
24. See n. 4.
25. See n. 6.
26. See n. 4.
27. Ibid.
28. "Giving Money Away," interview with Henry Heald, *International Science and Technology*, Oct., 1966, p. 104.
29. *Time*, Oct. 21, 1966.
30. See n. 6.
31. "The Annual Report of the President on Activities Carried Out under Public Law 480," 89th Congress, as Amended, during the period Jan. 1 through Dec. 31, 1965, dated June 30, 1966.
32. C. H. Bailey, *Constituents of Wheat and Wheat Products* (New York: Reinholt, 1944), p. 215. Nitrogen figure obtained from LeRoy Voris, National Academy of Sciences, Washington, D.C.

## CHAPTER 10

1. Georg Borgstrom, *The Hungry Planet* (New York: Macmillan, 1965), p. 474.
2. William H. Avery, Governor of Kansas, address before the organizational meeting of the Committee on the World Food Crisis, Washington, D.C., Dec. 9, 1965.
3. Senator George McGovern, Senate Committee on Agriculture and Forestry, 89th Cong., 2nd Sess., on S. 2157, S. 2826, S. 2932, S. 2933, S. 2995, and H.R. 14929, Mar. 2, 1966.
4. Harrison Brown, *The Challenge of Man's Future* (New York: Viking, 1954). p. 266.
5. Senator Hubert H. Humphrey, *Proceedings of the National Conference*, American Food for Peace Council, Food for Peace, U.S. Department of State, Washington, D.C., Sept. 30, 1963.
6. Editorial, *Life*, Mar. 4, 1966, p. 4.
7. Ibid.
8. Herman Kahn, director, Hudson Institute, in conversation with the author, Oct. 25, 1965.
9. Arthur Gordon, "The Deadly Art of Non-Living," *Woman's Day*, July 1966, p. 92.
10. John Horn, television review, *New York Herald Tribune*, Feb. 26, 1966.
11. See n. 8.
12. Eric Hoffer, "Making a Mass Elite," *Holiday*, Mar. 1966, p. 14.
13. Frank M. Coffin, "Some Perspectives on the Current Debates on Aid," *Department of State Bulletin*, Sept. 30, 1963, p. 515.
14. Walter Lippmann, *Miami Herald*, Dec. 22, 1965, p. 7A.
15. Ibid.
16. President Lyndon B. Johnson, in an address before the American Legion National Convention, Washington, D.C., Aug. 30, 1966.
17. Ibid.
18. Abraham J. Multer, Hearings of the House Subcommittee on International Finance of the Committee on Banking and Currency, 89th Cong., 2nd Sess., Aug. 29, 1966.

# *Index*

Abernethy, Thomas G., 194
Abidjan, Ivory Coast, 104
abortion, 30, 36
Aden, 226
Afghanistan, 119
  as food aid recipient, 12-13, 226
  physicians in, 31
  population estimates for, 12-13
Africa:
  agricultural research in, 76, 77
  caloric supply levels in, 50-51
  corn as food in, 123, 127, 137
  criticism of U.S. in, 239
  death rates in, 16
  export-import changes in, 43
  famines as inevitable for, 8
  farmers in population of, 31
  fertilizer use in, 81
  food production vs. population in,
    45, 53, 55
  illiteracy rate in, 30
  leadership in, 105, 117
  and modernization, 101, 104-107,
    119
  *see also under names of countries*
age, population:
  and birth rate, 20, 21-22
  and caloric requirements, 52, 54
  young people in, 18, 20-21, 22,
    37, 52, 137
Agency for International Development (AID), 167, 197
  and agricultural research, 76-77
  and land reform, 88
  and policy changes, 242

Agency for International Development (AID) *(cont.)*
  and private enterprise, 66, 92, 93
  Tunisian program of, 215-216
Agricultural Trade Development and
  Assistance Act, *see* Public Law
  480
agriculture:
  collectivized, 145, 149, 154, 156,
    162
  downgrading of, 42, 57, 75-76,
    149-150, 151
  education in field of, 75-77
  and farm families, 30-31
  hydroponic, 66-67
  and irrigation, 68-69, 82-84, 230
  land available for, 29, 37-39, 45-
    47, 52, 84-87, 230
  private enterprise for development
    of, 91-95
  and Public Law 480, effect on,
    175-178
  research in, 29, 62-69, 71-97, 152-
    155, 156-157, 159-160, 163-164,
    220-221, 222, 223-225, 230
  technical aid for, 74-75, 196-197
  tropical, 9, 46-47, 63, 73-78, 82-
    86, 93, 223-224
  *see also* food production
Agriculture, Department of:
  on caloric consumption, 50
  food production and aid need
    projections by, 135-141, 209
  per acre yield data from, 46
  and Public Law 480, 183, 185